THE BOOK OF PROBLEMS:

PREALGEBRA

Brian K. Saltzer
Eric Stimmel

The Book of Problems Series

Printed in the United States of America

9 10 11 12 V0CR 14 13 12 11

ISBN 0-536-96602-8

2005360640

AP

PEARSON CUSTOM PUBLISHING
75 Arlington Street, Suite 300, Boston, MA 02116
A Pearson Education Company

Pittsburgh

About This Book

The Book of Problems series originated in the fact that students simply don't need another textbook on Algebra, Calculus, etc. There are already wonderful textbooks on the market in almost every area of mathematics and science. What struggling students do need, however, are more detailed worked examples than are normally found in even the best textbooks. To solve this problem, every book in the Book of Problems series contains hundreds of problems with both answers and detailed, worked solutions.

In this volume, *The Book of Problems - Prealgebra*, each of the major concepts in a standard pre-algebra course is given its own section and problems. After a list of the problems for a concept, the answers are given so that students can compare their answers to the correct ones. Following the answers are detailed worked solutions to each problem. The answers are given first because many students do not want to see a detailed worked solution immediately upon finding that their answer is not the correct one.

At the end of the book are two Final Exams that test whether or not the student has grasped all of the concepts in the book. Because students must be able to solve problems regardless of the order that they appear on their college/high school exams, the Finals are not in the same concept order as that given in the Table of Contents. The first Final Exam groups concepts that are similar (although not it the same order as presented in the book) and the second Final Exam completely randomizes the concepts and problems. As with every other problem in the Book of Problems series, both answers and detailed, worked solutions to all Final Exam questions are included in the book.

Our sincere hope is that this book will aid you in your goal of attaining both a higher course grade and a deeper understanding of Prealgebra.

BKS
EPS

TABLE OF CONTENTS

ADDING AND SUBTRACTING WHOLE NUMBERS

Perform each of the following additions and subtractions.

1. $2+7=$

2. $3+6+5=$

3. $4+(8+9)=$

4. $(2+1)+12=$

5. $(5+7)+(1+8)=$

6. $8-6=$

7. $10-2-3=$

8. $(15-2)-8=$

9. $(2+9)-5=$

10. $(17-4)-9=$

11. $\begin{array}{r} 27 \\ +\ 8 \\ \hline \end{array}$

12. $\begin{array}{r} 28 \\ +\ 13 \\ \hline \end{array}$

13. $\begin{array}{r} 597 \\ +\ 14 \\ \hline \end{array}$

14. $\begin{array}{r} 74 \\ 139 \\ +\ 27 \\ \hline \end{array}$

15. $\begin{array}{r} 215 \\ 382 \\ +\ 433 \\ \hline \end{array}$

16. $\begin{array}{r} 9 \\ -\ 8 \\ \hline \end{array}$

17. $\begin{array}{r} 10 \\ -\ 6 \\ \hline \end{array}$

18. $\begin{array}{r} 22 \\ -\ 9 \\ \hline \end{array}$

19. $\begin{array}{r} 235 \\ -\ 17 \\ \hline \end{array}$

20. $\begin{array}{r} 576 \\ -\ 298 \\ \hline \end{array}$

Notes

Notes

Answer Key

1. 9
2. 14
3. 21
4. 15
5. 21
6. 2
7. 5
8. 5
9. 6
10. 4
11. 35
12. 41
13. 611
14. 240
15. 1030
16. 1
17. 4
18. 13
19. 218
20. 278

Solutions

1. $2 + 7 = 9$

2. $3 + 6 + 5 = 14$

3. $4 + (8 + 9) = 4 + (17) = 21$

4. $(2 + 1) + 12 = (3) + 12 = 15$

5. $(5 + 7) + (1 + 8) = (12) + (9) = 21$

6. $8 - 6 = 2$

7. $10 - 2 - 3 = 5$

8. $(15 - 2) - 8 = (13) - 8 = 5$

9. $(2 + 9) - 5 = (11) - 5 = 6$

10. $(17 - 4) - 9 = (13) - 9 = 4$

11.
$$\begin{array}{r} 27 \\ + \ 8 \\ \hline 35 \end{array}$$

12.
$$\begin{array}{r} 28 \\ + 13 \\ \hline 41 \end{array}$$

13.
$$\begin{array}{r} 597 \\ + \ 14 \\ \hline 611 \end{array}$$

14.
$$\begin{array}{r} 74 \\ 139 \\ + \ 27 \\ \hline 240 \end{array}$$

15.
$$\begin{array}{r} 215 \\ 382 \\ + 433 \\ \hline 1030 \end{array}$$

16.
$$\begin{array}{r} 9 \\ - \ 8 \\ \hline 1 \end{array}$$

17.
$$\begin{array}{r} 10 \\ - \ 6 \\ \hline 4 \end{array}$$

18.
$$\begin{array}{r} 22 \\ - \ 9 \\ \hline 13 \end{array}$$

19.
$$\begin{array}{r} 235 \\ - \ 17 \\ \hline 218 \end{array}$$

20.
$$\begin{array}{r} 576 \\ - 298 \\ \hline 278 \end{array}$$

MULTIPLYING AND DIVIDING WHOLE NUMBERS

Perform each of the following multiplications and divisions.

1. $2 \times 7 =$

2. $3 \times 9 =$

3. $5 \times (2 \times 6) =$

4. $(3 \times 4) \times 2 =$

5. $(1 \times 7) \times (3 \times 2) =$

6. $6 \div 2 =$

7. $48 \div 3 =$

8. $72 \div 6 =$

9. $100 \div 20 =$

10. $(100 \div 10) \div 2 =$

11. $\begin{array}{r} 9 \\ \times\, 2 \\ \hline \end{array}$

12. $\begin{array}{r} 13 \\ \times\, 5 \\ \hline \end{array}$

13. $\begin{array}{r} 27 \\ \times\, 63 \\ \hline \end{array}$

14. $\begin{array}{r} 216 \\ \times\, 537 \\ \hline \end{array}$

15. $\begin{array}{r} 7429 \\ \times\, 36 \\ \hline \end{array}$

16. $8 \overline{)56}$

17. $7 \overline{)420}$

18. $12 \overline{)60}$

19. $3 \overline{)2931}$

20. $120 \overline{)3600}$

Notes

5

Notes

Answer Key

1. 14
2. 27
3. 60
4. 24
5. 42
6. 3
7. 16
8. 12
9. 5
10. 5
11. 18
12. 65
13. 1701
14. 115,992
15. 267,444
16. 7
17. 60
18. 5
19. 977
20. 30

Solutions

1. $2 \times 7 = 14$

2. $3 \times 9 = 27$

3. $5 \times (2 \times 6) = 5 \times (12) = 60$

4. $(3 \times 4) \times 2 = (12) \times 2 = 24$

5. $(1 \times 7) \times (3 \times 2) = (7) \times (6) = 42$

6. $6 \div 2 = 3$

7. $48 \div 3 = 16$

8. $72 \div 6 = 12$

9. $100 \div 20 = 5$

10. $(100 \div 10) \div 2 = (10) \div 2 = 5$

11.
$$
\begin{array}{r}
9 \\
\times\ 2 \\
\hline
18
\end{array}
$$

12.
$$
\begin{array}{r}
13 \\
\times\ 5 \\
\hline
65
\end{array}
$$

13.
$$
\begin{array}{r}
27 \\
\times\ 63 \\
\hline
81 \\
+\ 162 \\
\hline
1701
\end{array}
$$

14.
$$
\begin{array}{r}
216 \\
\times\ 537 \\
\hline
1512 \\
648 \\
+\ 1080 \\
\hline
115992
\end{array}
$$

15.
$$
\begin{array}{r}
7429 \\
\times\ 36 \\
\hline
44574 \\
+\ 22287 \\
\hline
267444
\end{array}
$$

16.
$$
\begin{array}{r}
7 \\
8\overline{)56} \\
56 \\
\hline
0
\end{array}
$$

17.
$$
\begin{array}{r}
60 \\
7\overline{)420} \\
42 \\
\hline
00
\end{array}
$$

18.
$$
\begin{array}{r}
5 \\
12\overline{)60} \\
60 \\
\hline
0
\end{array}
$$

19.
$$
\begin{array}{r}
977 \\
3\overline{)2931} \\
27 \\
\hline
23 \\
21 \\
\hline
21 \\
21 \\
\hline
0
\end{array}
$$

20.
$$
\begin{array}{r}
30 \\
120\overline{)3600} \\
360 \\
\hline
00
\end{array}
$$

THE REAL NUMBER LINE

Plot each of the following on a number line.

1. 3

2. -1

3. 0

4. $2\dfrac{1}{2}$

5. -4.5

6. 1.2

7. $-2\dfrac{1}{3}$

8. 0.4

9. -0.3

10. $\dfrac{1}{6}$

Notes

Solutions

1.

```
  -5 -4 -3 -2 -1  0  1  2  3  4  5
```

2.

```
  -5 -4 -3 -2 -1  0  1  2  3  4  5
```

3.

```
  -5 -4 -3 -2 -1  0  1  2  3  4  5
```

4.

$2\frac{1}{2}$

```
  -5 -4 -3 -2 -1  0  1  2  3  4  5
```

5.

-4.5

```
  -5 -4 -3 -2 -1  0  1  2  3  4  5
```

6.

1.2

```
  -5 -4 -3 -2 -1  0  1  2  3  4  5
```

7.

$-2\frac{1}{3}$

```
  -5 -4 -3 -2 -1  0  1  2  3  4  5
```

8.

0.4

```
  -5 -4 -3 -2 -1  0  1  2  3  4  5
```

9.

-0.3

```
  -5 -4 -3 -2 -1  0  1  2  3  4  5
```

10.

$\frac{1}{6}$

```
  -5 -4 -3 -2 -1  0  1  2  3  4  5
```

GRAPHING
INTERVALS

Using a real number line, graph each of the following intervals.

1. $(3, 7)$

2. $(-4, 1)$

3. $(-2, 2]$

4. $[-7, -4]$

5. $\left(\dfrac{1}{2}, 4\dfrac{1}{2}\right)$

6. $\left[0.25, 6\dfrac{1}{2}\right)$

7. $\left(-3\dfrac{3}{4}, -1\dfrac{1}{2}\right]$

8. $(-0.5, 0.75)$

9. $[1.6, 4.3)$

10. $[0, 0.9]$

Notes

Notes

Solutions

1. $(3, 7)$

2. $(-4, 1)$

3. $(-2, 2]$

4. $[-7, -4]$

5. $\left(\dfrac{1}{2}, 4\dfrac{1}{2}\right)$

6. $\left[0.25, 6\dfrac{1}{2}\right)$

7. $\left(-3\dfrac{3}{4}, -1\dfrac{1}{2}\right]$

8. $(-0.5, 0.75)$

9. $[1.6, 4.3)$

10. $[0, 0.9]$

LEAST COMMON MULTIPLE (LCM)

Find the Least Common Multiple (LCM) of each of the following sets of numbers.

1. 3, 6
2. 2, 7
3. 2, 4, 5
4. 1, 6, 7
5. 2, 13
6. 2, 3, 5, 7
7. 2, 3, 9, 18
8. 3, 17, 38
9. 5, 47, 94
10. 7, 13, 17

Notes

Solutions

1. 6
2. 14
3. 20
4. 42
5. 26
6. 210
7. 18
8. 1938
9. 470
10. 1547

PRIME
FACTORIZATION

Factor each of the following into its prime factors. If the number is already prime, identify it as so.

1. 6
2. 24
3. 35
4. 120
5. 512
6. 47
7. 1000
8. 1692
9. 5376
10. 91

Notes

Notes

Answer Key

1. $6 = 2 \cdot 3$

2. $24 = 2 \cdot 2 \cdot 2 \cdot 3$

3. $35 = 5 \cdot 7$

4. $120 = 2 \cdot 2 \cdot 2 \cdot 3 \cdot 5$

5. $512 = 2 \cdot 2 \cdot 2 \cdot 2 \cdot 2 \cdot 2 \cdot 2 \cdot 2 \cdot 2$

6. Prime

7. $1000 = 2 \cdot 2 \cdot 2 \cdot 5 \cdot 5 \cdot 5$

8. $1692 = 2 \cdot 2 \cdot 3 \cdot 3 \cdot 47$

9. $5376 = 2 \cdot 2 \cdot 2 \cdot 2 \cdot 2 \cdot 2 \cdot 2 \cdot 2 \cdot 3 \cdot 7$

10. Prime

Solutions

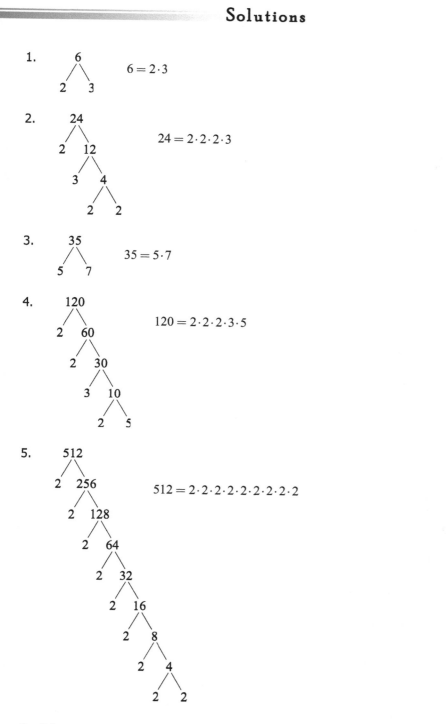

1.
$$6 = 2 \cdot 3$$

2.
$$24 = 2 \cdot 2 \cdot 2 \cdot 3$$

3.
$$35 = 5 \cdot 7$$

4.
$$120 = 2 \cdot 2 \cdot 2 \cdot 3 \cdot 5$$

5.
$$512 = 2 \cdot 2 \cdot 2 \cdot 2 \cdot 2 \cdot 2 \cdot 2 \cdot 2 \cdot 2$$

6. Prime

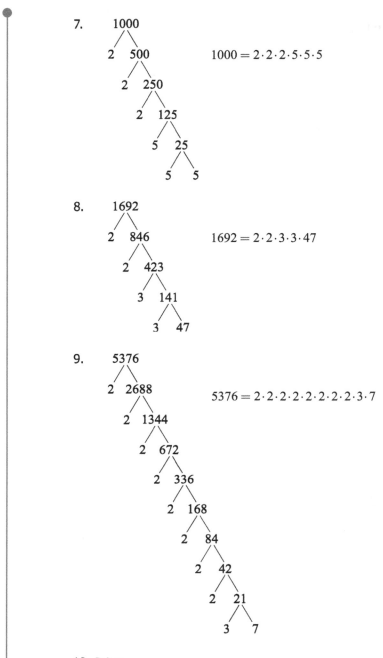

7. $1000 = 2 \cdot 2 \cdot 2 \cdot 5 \cdot 5 \cdot 5$

8. $1692 = 2 \cdot 2 \cdot 3 \cdot 3 \cdot 47$

9. $5376 = 2 \cdot 2 \cdot 2 \cdot 2 \cdot 2 \cdot 2 \cdot 2 \cdot 2 \cdot 3 \cdot 7$

10. Prime

REDUCING FRACTIONS USING THE METHOD OF COMMON FACTORS

Use the method of common factors to reduce each of the following expressions to its lowest form.

1. $\dfrac{4}{14}$

2. $\dfrac{4}{12}$

3. $\dfrac{30}{180}$

4. $\dfrac{32}{128}$

5. $\dfrac{25}{400}$

6. $\dfrac{72}{140}$

7. $\dfrac{125}{385}$

8. $\dfrac{70}{7}$

9. $\dfrac{36}{12}$

10. $\dfrac{1200}{24}$

Notes

Answer Key

1. $\dfrac{2}{7}$

2. $\dfrac{1}{3}$

3. $\dfrac{1}{6}$

4. $\dfrac{1}{4}$

5. $\dfrac{1}{16}$

6. $\dfrac{18}{35}$

7. $\dfrac{25}{77}$

8. 10

9. 3

10. 50

Solutions

1. $\dfrac{4}{14} = \dfrac{\cancel{2} \cdot 2}{\cancel{2} \cdot 7} = \dfrac{2}{7}$

2. $\dfrac{4}{12} = \dfrac{1 \cdot \cancel{2} \cdot \cancel{2}}{\cancel{2} \cdot \cancel{2} \cdot 3} = \dfrac{1}{3}$

3. $\dfrac{30}{180} = \dfrac{1 \cdot \cancel{2} \cdot \cancel{3} \cdot \cancel{5}}{2 \cdot \cancel{2} \cdot \cancel{3} \cdot 3 \cdot \cancel{5}} = \dfrac{1}{2 \cdot 3} = \dfrac{1}{6}$

4. $\dfrac{32}{128} = \dfrac{1 \cdot \cancel{2} \cdot \cancel{2} \cdot \cancel{2} \cdot \cancel{2} \cdot \cancel{2}}{\cancel{2} \cdot \cancel{2} \cdot \cancel{2} \cdot \cancel{2} \cdot \cancel{2} \cdot 2 \cdot 2} = \dfrac{1}{2 \cdot 2} = \dfrac{1}{4}$

5. $\dfrac{25}{400} = \dfrac{1 \cdot \cancel{5} \cdot \cancel{5}}{2 \cdot 2 \cdot 2 \cdot 2 \cdot \cancel{5} \cdot \cancel{5}} = \dfrac{1}{2 \cdot 2 \cdot 2 \cdot 2} = \dfrac{1}{16}$

6. $\dfrac{72}{140} = \dfrac{\cancel{2} \cdot \cancel{2} \cdot 2 \cdot 3 \cdot 3}{\cancel{2} \cdot \cancel{2} \cdot 5 \cdot 7} = \dfrac{2 \cdot 3 \cdot 3}{5 \cdot 7} = \dfrac{18}{35}$

7. $\dfrac{125}{385} = \dfrac{\cancel{5} \cdot 5 \cdot 5}{\cancel{5} \cdot 7 \cdot 11} = \dfrac{5 \cdot 5}{7 \cdot 11} = \dfrac{25}{77}$

8. $\dfrac{70}{7} = \dfrac{\cancel{7} \cdot 2 \cdot 5}{\cancel{7}} = 2 \cdot 5 = 10$

9. $\dfrac{36}{12} = \dfrac{\cancel{2} \cdot \cancel{2} \cdot \cancel{3} \cdot 3}{\cancel{2} \cdot \cancel{2} \cdot \cancel{3}} = 3$

10. $\dfrac{1200}{24} = \dfrac{\cancel{2} \cdot \cancel{2} \cdot \cancel{2} \cdot 2 \cdot \cancel{3} \cdot 5 \cdot 5}{\cancel{2} \cdot \cancel{2} \cdot \cancel{2} \cdot \cancel{3}} = 2 \cdot 5 \cdot 5 = 50$

ADDING, SUBTRACTING, MULTIPLYING, AND DIVIDING FRACTIONS

Add, subtract, multiply or divide each of the following fractions. Record your answer in lowest terms.

1. $\dfrac{1}{3} + \dfrac{5}{6} =$

2. $\dfrac{2}{3} + \dfrac{1}{5} =$

3. $\dfrac{5}{7} - \dfrac{1}{3} =$

4. $\dfrac{8}{9} - \dfrac{1}{2} =$

5. $\dfrac{1}{2} + \dfrac{1}{3} + \dfrac{1}{5} =$

6. $\dfrac{1}{2} \times \dfrac{3}{7} =$

7. $\dfrac{3}{5} \times \dfrac{1}{6} =$

8. $\dfrac{3}{5} \times \dfrac{1}{2} \times \dfrac{7}{11} =$

9. $\dfrac{\frac{2}{3}}{\frac{1}{5}} =$

10. $\dfrac{\frac{3}{4}}{\frac{2}{7}} =$

11. $\dfrac{\frac{3}{5}}{\frac{4}{3}} =$

12. $\dfrac{3}{7} \times \left(\dfrac{2}{3} + \dfrac{1}{5} \right) =$

13. $\dfrac{\left(\frac{3}{7} + \frac{1}{2} \right)}{\frac{2}{5}} =$

14. $\dfrac{\frac{3}{11}}{\left(\frac{1}{4} + \frac{2}{5} \right)} =$

15. $\dfrac{\left(\frac{1}{2} + \frac{1}{3} \right)}{\left(\frac{1}{4} + \frac{1}{5} \right)} =$

Notes

Answer Key

1. $1\frac{1}{6}$

2. $\frac{13}{15}$

3. $\frac{8}{21}$

4. $\frac{7}{18}$

5. $1\frac{1}{30}$

6. $\frac{3}{14}$

7. $\frac{1}{10}$

8. $\frac{21}{110}$

9. $3\frac{1}{3}$

10. $2\frac{5}{8}$

11. $\frac{9}{20}$

12. $\frac{13}{35}$

13. $2\frac{9}{28}$

14. $\frac{60}{143}$

15. $1\frac{23}{27}$

Solutions

1. Using a common denominator of 6, we get:

$$\frac{1}{3} + \frac{5}{6} = \frac{2}{6} + \frac{5}{6} = \frac{7}{6} = 1\frac{1}{6}$$

2. Using a common denominator of 15, we get:

$$\frac{2}{3} + \frac{1}{5} = \frac{10}{15} + \frac{3}{15} = \frac{13}{15}$$

3. Using a common denominator of 21, we get:

$$\frac{5}{7} - \frac{1}{3} = \frac{15}{21} - \frac{7}{21} = \frac{8}{21}$$

4. Using a common denominator of 18, we get:

$$\frac{8}{9} - \frac{1}{2} = \frac{16}{18} - \frac{9}{18} = \frac{7}{18}$$

5. Using a common denominator of 30, we get:

$$\frac{1}{2} + \frac{1}{3} + \frac{1}{5} = \frac{1(3)(5)}{30} + \frac{1(2)(5)}{30} + \frac{1(2)(3)}{30}$$

$$= \frac{15}{30} + \frac{10}{30} + \frac{6}{30} = \frac{31}{30} = 1\frac{1}{30}$$

6. $\dfrac{1}{2} \times \dfrac{3}{7} = \dfrac{1 \times 3}{2 \times 7} = \dfrac{3}{14}$

7. $\dfrac{3}{5} \times \dfrac{1}{6} = \dfrac{3 \times 1}{5 \times 6} = \dfrac{3}{30} = \dfrac{1}{10}$

8. $\dfrac{3}{5} \times \dfrac{1}{2} \times \dfrac{7}{11} = \dfrac{3 \times 1 \times 7}{5 \times 2 \times 11} = \dfrac{21}{110}$

9. $\dfrac{\frac{2}{3}}{\frac{1}{5}} = \dfrac{2}{3} \times \dfrac{5}{1} = \dfrac{2 \times 5}{3 \times 1} = \dfrac{10}{3} = 3\dfrac{1}{3}$

10. $\dfrac{\frac{3}{4}}{\frac{2}{7}} = \dfrac{3}{4} \times \dfrac{7}{2} = \dfrac{3 \times 7}{4 \times 2} = \dfrac{21}{8} = 2\dfrac{5}{8}$

11. $\dfrac{\dfrac{3}{5}}{\dfrac{4}{3}} = \dfrac{3}{5} \times \dfrac{3}{4} = \dfrac{3 \times 3}{5 \times 4} = \dfrac{9}{20}$

12. We first use a common denominator of 15 to combine the two fractions inside the parentheses:

$$\frac{3}{7} \times \left(\frac{2}{3} + \frac{1}{5}\right) = \frac{3}{7} \times \left(\frac{10}{15} + \frac{3}{15}\right) = \frac{3}{7} \times \left(\frac{13}{15}\right) = \frac{3}{7} \times \frac{13}{15}$$

Next, we execute the required multiplication:

$$\frac{3}{7} \times \frac{13}{15} = \frac{3 \times 13}{7 \times 15} = \frac{39}{105} = \frac{13}{35}$$

Thus,

$$\frac{3}{7} \times \left(\frac{2}{3} + \frac{1}{5}\right) = \frac{13}{35}$$

13. First, we add the two fractions in the numerator using a common denominator of 14:

$$\frac{\left(\dfrac{3}{7} + \dfrac{1}{2}\right)}{\dfrac{2}{5}} = \frac{\dfrac{6}{14} + \dfrac{7}{14}}{\dfrac{2}{5}} = \frac{\dfrac{13}{14}}{\dfrac{2}{5}}$$

Next we perform the required division:

$$\frac{\dfrac{13}{14}}{\dfrac{2}{5}} = \frac{13}{14} \times \frac{5}{2} = \frac{13 \times 5}{14 \times 2} = \frac{65}{28} = 2\frac{9}{28}$$

Thus,

$$\frac{\left(\dfrac{3}{7} + \dfrac{1}{2}\right)}{\dfrac{2}{5}} = 2\frac{9}{28}$$

14. First, we add the two fractions in the denominator using a common denominator of 20:

$$\frac{\frac{3}{11}}{\left(\frac{1}{4}+\frac{2}{5}\right)} = \frac{\frac{3}{11}}{\frac{5}{20}+\frac{8}{20}} = \frac{\frac{3}{11}}{\frac{13}{20}}$$

Next, we divide our two fractions:

$$\frac{\frac{3}{11}}{\frac{13}{20}} = \frac{3}{11} \times \frac{20}{13} = \frac{60}{143}$$

Thus,

$$\frac{\frac{3}{11}}{\left(\frac{1}{4}+\frac{2}{5}\right)} = \frac{60}{143}$$

15. First, we add the two fractions in the numerator using a common denominator of 6:

$$\frac{\left(\frac{1}{2}+\frac{1}{3}\right)}{\left(\frac{1}{4}+\frac{1}{5}\right)} = \frac{\frac{3}{6}+\frac{2}{6}}{\frac{1}{4}+\frac{1}{5}} = \frac{\frac{5}{6}}{\frac{1}{4}+\frac{1}{5}}$$

Next, we add the two fractions in the denominator using a common denominator of 20:

$$\frac{\frac{5}{6}}{\frac{1}{4}+\frac{1}{5}} = \frac{\frac{5}{6}}{\frac{5}{20}+\frac{4}{20}} = \frac{\frac{5}{6}}{\frac{9}{20}}$$

Lastly, we perform the required division:

$$\frac{\frac{5}{6}}{\frac{9}{20}} = \frac{5}{6} \times \frac{20}{9} = \frac{100}{54} = \frac{50}{27} = 1\frac{23}{27}$$

Thus,

$$\frac{\left(\frac{1}{2}+\frac{1}{3}\right)}{\left(\frac{1}{4}+\frac{1}{5}\right)} = 1\frac{23}{27}$$

ADDING, SUBTRACTING, MULTIPLYING, AND DIVIDING MIXED NUMBERS

9

Calculate each of the following and record your answer in lowest terms.

Notes

1. $1\dfrac{2}{5}+2\dfrac{2}{3}=$

2. $3\dfrac{1}{4}+6\dfrac{1}{3}=$

3. $5\dfrac{2}{7}-1\dfrac{1}{3}=$

4. $7\dfrac{1}{5}-2\dfrac{1}{6}=$

5. $3\dfrac{1}{5}+2\dfrac{1}{3}+4\dfrac{1}{6}=$

6. $9\dfrac{1}{4}+2\dfrac{1}{2}-3\dfrac{1}{5}=$

7. $2\dfrac{1}{5}\times6\dfrac{1}{4}=$

8. $3\dfrac{1}{4}\times5\dfrac{1}{7}=$

9. $9\dfrac{1}{2}\times6\dfrac{1}{5}=$

10. $\dfrac{2\dfrac{1}{5}}{1\dfrac{1}{3}}=$

11. $\dfrac{7\dfrac{1}{2}}{5\dfrac{2}{3}}=$

12. $\dfrac{6\dfrac{1}{4}}{15\dfrac{1}{2}}=$

13. $\dfrac{\left(1\dfrac{2}{3}+6\dfrac{3}{4}\right)}{5\dfrac{1}{2}}=$

14. $\dfrac{3\dfrac{2}{5}}{\left(1\dfrac{1}{4}+1\dfrac{2}{7}\right)}=$

15. $\dfrac{\left(3\dfrac{1}{4}+5\dfrac{1}{6}\right)}{\left(7\dfrac{1}{2}-2\dfrac{1}{9}\right)}=$

Notes

Answer Key

1. $4\frac{1}{15}$

2. $9\frac{7}{12}$

3. $3\frac{20}{21}$

4. $5\frac{1}{30}$

5. $9\frac{7}{10}$

6. $8\frac{11}{20}$

7. $13\frac{3}{4}$

8. $16\frac{5}{7}$

9. $58\frac{9}{10}$

10. $1\frac{13}{20}$

11. $1\frac{11}{34}$

12. $\frac{25}{62}$

13. $1\frac{35}{66}$

14. $1\frac{121}{355}$

15. $1\frac{109}{194}$

Solutions

1. First, we express each mixed number as an improper fraction:

$$1\frac{2}{5} + 2\frac{2}{3} = \frac{7}{5} + \frac{8}{3}$$

Next, we add the two fractions using a common denominator of 15:

$$\frac{7}{5} + \frac{8}{3} = \frac{21}{15} + \frac{40}{15} = \frac{61}{15}$$

Finally, we express our answer as a mixed number:

$$\frac{61}{15} = 4\frac{1}{15}$$

Thus,

$$1\frac{2}{5} + 2\frac{2}{3} = 4\frac{1}{15}$$

2. Expressing both mixed numbers as improper fractions, we have:

$$3\frac{1}{4} + 6\frac{1}{3} = \frac{13}{4} + \frac{19}{3}$$

Next, we add our two fractions using a common denominator of 12:

$$\frac{13}{4} + \frac{19}{3} = \frac{39}{12} + \frac{76}{12} = \frac{115}{12}$$

Expressing our answer as a mixed number, we get:

$$\frac{115}{12} = 9\frac{7}{12}$$

Thus,

$$3\frac{1}{4} + 6\frac{1}{3} = 9\frac{7}{12}$$

3. Expressing both mixed numbers as improper fractions:

$$5\frac{2}{7} - 1\frac{1}{3} = \frac{37}{7} - \frac{4}{3}$$

Subtracting them using a common denominator of 21:

$$\frac{37}{7} - \frac{4}{3} = \frac{111}{21} - \frac{28}{21} = \frac{83}{21}$$

Expressing our result as a mixed number:

$$\frac{83}{21} = 3\frac{20}{21}$$

Thus,

$$5\frac{2}{7} - 1\frac{1}{3} = 3\frac{20}{21}$$

4. Expressing both mixed numbers as improper fractions:

$$7\frac{1}{5} - 2\frac{1}{6} = \frac{36}{5} - \frac{13}{6}$$

Subtracting the two fractions using a common denominator of 30:

$$\frac{36}{5} - \frac{13}{6} = \frac{216}{30} - \frac{65}{30} = \frac{151}{30}$$

Expressing our result as a mixed number:

$$\frac{151}{30} = 5\frac{1}{30}$$

Thus,

$$7\frac{1}{5} - 2\frac{1}{6} = 5\frac{1}{30}$$

5. Expressing all three mixed numbers as improper fractions:

$$3\frac{1}{5} + 2\frac{1}{3} + 4\frac{1}{6} = \frac{16}{5} + \frac{7}{3} + \frac{25}{6}$$

Adding the three fractions using a common denominator of 30:

$$\frac{16}{5} + \frac{7}{3} + \frac{25}{6} = \frac{96}{30} + \frac{70}{30} + \frac{125}{30} = \frac{291}{30}$$

Expressing the result as a mixed number:

$$9\frac{21}{30} = 9\frac{7}{10}$$

Thus,

$$3\frac{1}{5} + 2\frac{1}{3} + 4\frac{1}{6} = 9\frac{7}{10}$$

6. Expressing all three mixed numbers as improper fractions:

$$9\frac{1}{4} + 2\frac{1}{2} - 3\frac{1}{5} = \frac{37}{4} + \frac{5}{2} - \frac{16}{5}$$

Performing the required addition and subtraction using a common denominator of 20:

$$\frac{37}{4} + \frac{5}{2} - \frac{16}{5} = \frac{185}{20} + \frac{50}{20} - \frac{64}{20} = \frac{171}{20}$$

Expressing the result as a mixed number:

$$\frac{171}{20} = 8\frac{11}{20}$$

Thus,

$$9\frac{1}{4} + 2\frac{1}{2} - 3\frac{1}{5} = 8\frac{11}{20}$$

7. Expressing the two mixed numbers as improper fractions:

$$2\frac{1}{5} \times 6\frac{1}{4} = \frac{11}{5} \times \frac{25}{4}$$

Multiplying:

$$\frac{11}{5} \times \frac{25}{4} = \frac{11 \times 25}{5 \times 4} = \frac{275}{20}$$

Expressing the result as a mixed number, we have:

$$2\frac{1}{5} \times 6\frac{1}{4} = \frac{275}{20}$$

$$2\frac{1}{5} \times 6\frac{1}{4} = 13\frac{3}{4}$$

8. Expressing the two mixed numbers as improper fractions:

$$3\frac{1}{4} \times 5\frac{1}{7} = \frac{13}{4} \times \frac{36}{7}$$

Multiplying:

$$\frac{13}{4} \times \frac{36}{7} = \frac{13 \times 36}{4 \times 7} = \frac{468}{28}$$

Expressing our answer as a mixed number in lowest terms, we get:

$$3\frac{1}{4} \times 5\frac{1}{7} = \frac{468}{28}$$

$$3\frac{1}{4} \times 5\frac{1}{7} = 16\frac{5}{7}$$

9. Expressing both mixed numbers as improper fractions:

$$9\frac{1}{2} \times 6\frac{1}{5} = \frac{19}{2} \times \frac{31}{5}$$

Multiplying:

$$\frac{19}{2} \times \frac{31}{5} = \frac{19 \times 31}{2 \times 5} = \frac{589}{10}$$

Thus,

$$9\frac{1}{2} \times 6\frac{1}{5} = \frac{589}{10}$$

$$9\frac{1}{2} \times 6\frac{1}{5} = 58\frac{9}{10}$$

10. Expressing both mixed numbers as improper fractions:

$$\frac{2\frac{1}{5}}{1\frac{1}{3}} = \frac{\frac{11}{5}}{\frac{4}{3}}$$

Dividing:

$$\frac{\frac{11}{5}}{\frac{4}{3}} = \frac{11}{5} \times \frac{3}{4} = \frac{11 \times 3}{5 \times 4} = \frac{33}{20}$$

Thus,

$$\frac{2\frac{1}{5}}{1\frac{1}{3}} = \frac{33}{20}$$

$$\frac{2\frac{1}{5}}{1\frac{1}{3}} = 1\frac{13}{20}$$

11. Expressing both mixed numbers as improper fractions:

$$\frac{7\frac{1}{2}}{5\frac{2}{3}} = \frac{\frac{15}{2}}{\frac{17}{3}}$$

Dividing:

$$\frac{\frac{15}{2}}{\frac{17}{3}} = \frac{15}{2} \times \frac{3}{17} = \frac{15 \times 3}{2 \times 17} = \frac{45}{34}$$

Thus,

$$\frac{7\frac{1}{2}}{5\frac{2}{3}} = \frac{45}{34}$$

$$\frac{7\frac{1}{2}}{5\frac{2}{3}} = 1\frac{11}{34}$$

12. Expressing both mixed numbers as improper fractions:

$$\frac{6\frac{1}{4}}{15\frac{1}{2}} = \frac{\frac{25}{4}}{\frac{31}{2}}$$

Dividing:

$$\frac{\frac{25}{4}}{\frac{31}{2}} = \frac{25}{4} \times \frac{2}{31} = \frac{25 \times 2}{4 \times 31} = \frac{50}{124} = \frac{25}{62}$$

Thus,

$$\frac{6\frac{1}{4}}{15\frac{1}{2}} = \frac{25}{62}$$

13. Expressing all mixed numbers as improper fractions:

$$\frac{\left(1\frac{2}{3} + 6\frac{3}{4}\right)}{5\frac{1}{2}} = \frac{\frac{5}{3} + \frac{27}{4}}{\frac{11}{2}}$$

Adding the fractions in the numerator using a common denominator of 12:

$$\frac{\frac{5}{3} + \frac{27}{4}}{\frac{11}{2}} = \frac{\frac{20}{12} + \frac{81}{12}}{\frac{11}{2}} = \frac{\frac{101}{12}}{\frac{11}{2}}$$

Dividing:

$$\frac{\frac{101}{12}}{\frac{11}{2}} = \frac{101}{12} \times \frac{2}{11} = \frac{101 \times 2}{12 \times 11} = \frac{202}{132}$$

Thus,

$$\frac{\left(1\frac{2}{3} + 6\frac{3}{4}\right)}{5\frac{1}{2}} = \frac{202}{132} = 1\frac{70}{132} = 1\frac{35}{66}$$

14. Expressing all mixed numbers as improper fractions:

$$\frac{3\frac{2}{5}}{\left(1\frac{1}{4}+1\frac{2}{7}\right)}=\frac{\frac{17}{5}}{\frac{5}{4}+\frac{9}{7}}$$

Adding the fractions in the denominator using a common denominator of 28:

$$\frac{\frac{17}{5}}{\frac{5}{4}+\frac{9}{7}}=\frac{\frac{17}{5}}{\frac{35}{28}+\frac{36}{28}}=\frac{\frac{17}{5}}{\frac{71}{28}}$$

Dividing:

$$\frac{\frac{17}{5}}{\frac{71}{28}}=\frac{17}{5}\times\frac{28}{71}=\frac{17\times28}{5\times71}=\frac{476}{355}$$

Thus,

$$\frac{3\frac{2}{5}}{\left(1\frac{1}{4}+1\frac{2}{7}\right)}=\frac{476}{355}=1\frac{121}{355}$$

15. Expressing all four mixed numbers as improper fractions:

$$\frac{\left(3\frac{1}{4}+5\frac{1}{6}\right)}{\left(7\frac{1}{2}-2\frac{1}{9}\right)}=\frac{\frac{13}{4}+\frac{31}{6}}{\frac{15}{2}-\frac{19}{9}}$$

Using a common denominator of 24 in the numerator and a common denominator of 18 in the denominator:

$$\frac{\frac{13}{4}+\frac{31}{6}}{\frac{15}{2}-\frac{19}{9}}=\frac{\frac{78}{24}+\frac{124}{24}}{\frac{135}{18}-\frac{38}{18}}=\frac{\frac{202}{24}}{\frac{97}{18}}$$

Dividing:

$$\frac{\frac{202}{24}}{\frac{97}{18}}=\frac{202}{24}\times\frac{18}{97}=\frac{202\times18}{24\times97}=\frac{3636}{2328}$$

Thus,

$$\frac{\left(3\frac{1}{4}+5\frac{1}{6}\right)}{\left(7\frac{1}{2}-2\frac{1}{9}\right)}=\frac{3636}{2328}=1\frac{1308}{2328}=1\frac{109}{194}$$

ADDING, SUBTRACTING, MULTIPLYING, AND DIVIDING DECIMALS

Calculate each of the following.

Notes

1.   0.6
   + 0.9

2.   3.5
   + 0.7

3.   1.35
   + 0.6

4.   23.7
   + 6.92

5.   46.731
   + 2.009

6.   1.5
   − 0.7

7.   2.04
   − 0.97

8.   1.7
   − 0.04

9.   0.926
   − 0.08

10.   5.03
    − 1.99

11.   0.8
    × 0.6

12.   1.9
    × 0.5

13.   1.34
    × 6.7

14.   0.74
    × 2.5

15.   12.03
    × 0.16

16. 5⟌3.5

17. 0.6⟌4.2

18. 1.2⟌48

19. 0.4⟌2448

20. 7⟌0.00021

Answer Key

1. 1.5
2. 4.2
3. 1.95
4. 30.62
5. 48.740
6. 0.8
7. 1.07
8. 1.66
9. 0.846
10. 3.04
11. 0.48
12. 0.95
13. 8.978
14. 1.85
15. 1.9248
16. 0.7
17. 7.0
18. 40
19. 6120
20. 0.00003

Solutions

1.
$$\begin{array}{r} 0.6 \\ + 0.9 \\ \hline 1.5 \end{array}$$

2.
$$\begin{array}{r} 3.5 \\ + 0.7 \\ \hline 4.2 \end{array}$$

3.
$$\begin{array}{r} 1.35 \\ + 0.6 \\ \hline 1.95 \end{array}$$

4.
$$\begin{array}{r} 23.7 \\ + 6.92 \\ \hline 30.62 \end{array}$$

5.
$$\begin{array}{r} 46.731 \\ + 2.009 \\ \hline 48.740 \end{array}$$

6.
$$\begin{array}{r} 1.5 \\ - 0.7 \\ \hline 0.8 \end{array}$$

7.
$$\begin{array}{r} 2.04 \\ - 0.97 \\ \hline 1.07 \end{array}$$

8.
$$\begin{array}{r} 1.7 \\ - 0.04 \\ \hline 1.66 \end{array}$$

9.
$$\begin{array}{r} 0.926 \\ - 0.08 \\ \hline 0.846 \end{array}$$

10.
$$\begin{array}{r} 5.03 \\ - 1.99 \\ \hline 3.04 \end{array}$$

11.
$$\begin{array}{r} 0.8 \\ \times 0.6 \\ \hline 0.48 \end{array}$$

12.
$$\begin{array}{r} 1.9 \\ \times 0.5 \\ \hline 0.95 \end{array}$$

13.
$$\begin{array}{r} 1.34 \\ \times 6.7 \\ \hline 8.978 \end{array}$$

14.
$$\begin{array}{r} 0.74 \\ \times 2.5 \\ \hline 1.85 \end{array}$$

15.
$$\begin{array}{r} 12.03 \\ \times 0.16 \\ \hline 1.9248 \end{array}$$

16.
$$5 \overline{)3.5} \quad \frac{0.7}{}$$

17.
$$0.6 \overline{)4.2} \quad \frac{7.0}{}$$

18.
$$1.2 \overline{)48} \quad \frac{40}{}$$

19.
$$0.4 \overline{)2448} \quad \frac{6120}{}$$

20.
$$7 \overline{)0.00021} \quad \frac{0.00003}{}$$

ROUNDING DECIMALS

Correctly round each of the following:

1. 2.693   Round to the 1st decimal place.

2. 1.4872   Round to the 2nd decimal place.

3. 104.89   Round to the 1st decimal place.

4. 35.64   Round to the nearest whole number.

5. 29.324965   Round to the 5th decimal place.

6. 0.0000496   Round to the 6th decimal place.

7. 3.00009   Round to the 4th decimal place.

8. 876.1   Round to the nearest whole number.

9. 436.2984   Round to the 3rd decimal place.

10. 2.0005   Round to the 3rd decimal place.

Notes

Solutions

1. 2.7

2. 1.49

3. 104.9

4. 36

5. 29.32496

6. 0.000050

7. 3.0001

8. 876

9. 436.298

10. 2.000

CONVERTING BETWEEN
FRACTIONS AND DECIMALS

Convert the following fractional expressions into decimal expressions.

1. $\dfrac{1}{2}$

2. $\dfrac{3}{4}$

3. $\dfrac{4}{5}$

4. $\dfrac{2}{3}$

5. $\dfrac{7}{5}$

6. $\dfrac{17}{11}$

7. $2\dfrac{1}{4}$

8. $3\dfrac{1}{6}$

9. $\dfrac{100}{3}$

10. $\dfrac{2}{135}$

Convert the following decimal expressions into fractional expressions. Record your answer in lowest terms.

11. 0.4

12. 0.13

13. 0.007

14. 0.25

15. 0.00003

16. 1.15

17. 4.1

18. 0.1000001

19. 2.2424

20. 3.101

Notes

Answer Key

1. 0.5

2. 0.75

3. 0.8

4. $0.\overline{6}$

5. 1.4

6. $1.5\overline{45}$

7. 2.25

8. $3.1\overline{6}$

9. $33.\overline{3}$

10. $0.0\overline{148}$

11. $\dfrac{2}{5}$

12. $\dfrac{13}{100}$

13. $\dfrac{7}{1000}$

14. $\dfrac{1}{4}$

15. $\dfrac{3}{100,000}$

16. $1\dfrac{3}{20}$

17. $4\dfrac{1}{10}$

18. $\dfrac{1,000,001}{10,000,000}$

19. $2\dfrac{303}{1250}$

20. $3\dfrac{101}{1000}$

Solutions

1. $\dfrac{1}{2} = 2\overline{)1} = 0.5$

2. $\dfrac{3}{4} = 4\overline{)3} = 0.75$

3. $\dfrac{4}{5} = 5\overline{)4} = 0.8$

4. $\dfrac{2}{3} = 3\overline{)2} = 0.\overline{6}$

5. $\dfrac{7}{5} = 5\overline{)7} = 1.4$

6. $\dfrac{17}{11} = 11\overline{)17} = 1.5\overline{45}$

7. $2\dfrac{1}{4} = \dfrac{9}{4} = 4\overline{)9} = 2.25$

8. $3\dfrac{1}{6} = \dfrac{19}{6} = 6\overline{)19} = 3.1\overline{6}$

9. $\dfrac{100}{3} = 3\overline{)100} = 33.\overline{3}$

10. $\dfrac{2}{135} = 135\overline{)2} = 0.0\overline{148}$

11. $0.4 = \dfrac{4}{10} = \dfrac{2}{5}$

12. $0.13 = \dfrac{13}{100}$

13. $0.007 = \dfrac{7}{1000}$

14. $0.25 = \dfrac{25}{100} = \dfrac{1}{4}$

15. $0.00003 = \dfrac{3}{100,000}$

16. $1.15 = \dfrac{115}{100} = 1\dfrac{15}{100} = 1\dfrac{3}{20}$

17. $4.1 = \dfrac{41}{10} = 4\dfrac{1}{10}$

18. $0.1000001 = \dfrac{1,000,001}{10,000,000}$

19. $2.2424 = \dfrac{22,424}{10,000} = 2\dfrac{2424}{10,000} = 2\dfrac{303}{1250}$

20. $3.101 = \dfrac{3101}{1000} = 3\dfrac{101}{1000}$

SOLVING A
PROPORTION

Insert the correct number into the following boxes to make each statement a correct ratio.

1. $\dfrac{1}{2} = \dfrac{\square}{10}$

2. $\dfrac{3}{4} = \dfrac{9}{\square}$

3. $\dfrac{\square}{4} = \dfrac{6}{24}$

4. $\dfrac{5}{\square} = \dfrac{6}{30}$

5. $\dfrac{6}{\square} = \dfrac{2}{5} = \dfrac{\square}{100}$

6. $2 : \square = 10 : 30$

7. $\square : 12 = 1 : 4$

8. $3 : 15 = \square : 100$

9. $12 : 60 = 5 : \square$

10. $15 : \square = \square : 144 = 3 : 36$

Notes

Solutions

1. $\dfrac{1}{2} = \dfrac{\boxed{5}}{10}$

2. $\dfrac{3}{4} = \dfrac{9}{\boxed{12}}$

3. $\dfrac{\boxed{1}}{4} = \dfrac{6}{24}$

4. $\dfrac{5}{\boxed{25}} = \dfrac{6}{30}$

5. $\dfrac{6}{\boxed{15}} = \dfrac{2}{5} = \dfrac{\boxed{40}}{100}$

6. $2 : \boxed{6} = 10 : 30$

7. $\boxed{3} : 12 = 1 : 4$

8. $3 : 15 = \boxed{20} : 100$

9. $12 : 60 = 5 : \boxed{25}$

10. $15 : \boxed{180} = \boxed{12} : 144 = 3 : 36$

GREATER THAN
AND LESS THAN

Insert the appropriate symbol (>,<,=) into each of the following expressions.

1. $2 \,\square\, 1$

2. $3 \,\square\, 3.5$

3. $-1 \,\square\, -2$

4. $\dfrac{1}{2} \,\square\, 0.5$

5. $\dfrac{3}{5} \,\square\, 0.61$

6. $-\dfrac{1}{4} \,\square\, -0.24$

7. $\dfrac{1}{100} \,\square\, 0.001$

8. $-2 \,\square\, -\dfrac{100}{25}$

9. $\dfrac{22}{7} \,\square\, \dfrac{23}{8}$

10. $-\dfrac{1}{10} \,\square\, -0.1$

11. $2+(-3) \,\square\, -0.9$

12. $\dfrac{6}{-5} \,\square\, -1-0.3$

13. $-3+0.5 \,\square\, \dfrac{25}{-10}$

14. $(2-4)-6 \,\square\, 3\left(-\dfrac{8.1}{3}\right)$

15. $1.469-0.523 \,\square\, 0.0397+0.958$

Solutions

1. $2 \boxed{>} 1$

2. $3 \boxed{<} 3.5$

3. $-1 \boxed{>} -2$

4. $\dfrac{1}{2} \boxed{=} 0.5$

5. $\dfrac{3}{5} \boxed{<} 0.61$

6. $-\dfrac{1}{4} \boxed{<} -0.24$

7. $\dfrac{1}{100} \boxed{>} 0.001$

8. $-2 \boxed{>} -\dfrac{100}{25}$

9. $\dfrac{22}{7} \boxed{>} \dfrac{23}{8}$

10. $-\dfrac{1}{10} \boxed{=} -0.1$

11. $2+(-3) \boxed{\phantom{<}} -0.9$

    $-1 \boxed{\phantom{<}} -0.9$

    $-1 \boxed{<} -0.9$

12. $\dfrac{6}{-5} \boxed{\phantom{<}} -1-0.3$

    $-1.2 \boxed{\phantom{<}} -1.3$

    $-1.2 \boxed{>} -1.3$

13. $-3+0.5 \boxed{\phantom{<}} \dfrac{25}{-10}$

    $-2.5 \boxed{\phantom{<}} -2.5$

    $-2.5 \boxed{=} -2.5$

14. $(2-4)-6\,\square\,3\!\left(-\dfrac{8.1}{3}\right)$

   $(-2)-6\,\square\,-8.1$

   $-8\,\square\,-8.1$

   $-8\,\boxed{>}\,-8.1$

15. $1.469-0.523\,\square\,0.0397+0.958$

   $0.946\,\square\,0.9977$

   $0.946\,\boxed{<}\,0.9977$

CALCULATING
A PERCENTAGE

Express each of the following decimals as a percentage.

1. 0.62   4. 1.20

2. 0.40   5. 0.002

3. 0.05

Express each of the following percentages as a decimal.

6. 25%   9. 4%

7. 30%   10. 0.7%

8. 165%

Express each of the following fractions as a percentage.

11. $\dfrac{1}{4}$ 14. $\dfrac{3}{2}$

12. $\dfrac{3}{5}$ 15. $\dfrac{2}{1000}$

13. $\dfrac{2}{7}$

Calculate each of the following.

16. 20% of 50   21. 37.25% of 60

17. 35% of 80   22. 150% of 200

18. 6% of 15   23. 0.02% of 500

19. 0.3% of 110   24. 38% of 16.5

20. 42.5% of 30   25. 42.75% of 120.45

Notes

Notes

1. $0.62 = 62\%$

2. $0.40 = 40\%$

3. $0.05 = 5\%$

4. $1.20 = 120\%$

5. $0.002 = 0.2\%$

6. $25\% = 0.25$

7. $30\% = 0.30$

8. $165\% = 1.65$

9. $4\% = 0.04$

10. $0.7\% = 0.007$

11. $\dfrac{1}{4} = 0.25 = 25\%$

12. $\dfrac{3}{5} = 0.60 = 60\%$

13. $\dfrac{2}{7} = 0.29 = 29\%$

14. $\dfrac{3}{2} = 1.50 = 150\%$

15. $\dfrac{2}{1000} = 0.002 = 0.2\%$

16. $0.20(50) = 10$

17. $0.35(80) = 28$

18. $0.06(15) = 0.9$

19. $0.003(110) = 0.33$

20. $0.425(30) = 12.75$

21. $0.3725(60) = 22.35$

22. $1.5(200) = 300$

23. $0.0002(500) = 0.1$

24. $0.38(16.5) = 6.27$

25. $0.4275(120.45) = 51.49$

BASES AND EXPONENTS

Calculate each of the following exponential expressions.

Notes

1. 3^2

2. 2^3

3. 1^5

4. 0^4

5. $\left(\dfrac{1}{2}\right)^3$

6. $(0.1)^4$

7. $(-2)^4$

8. -2^4

9. $(-3)^3$

10. -3^3

11. $\left(-\dfrac{1}{3}\right)^2$

12. $(-0.4)^3$

13. -1^6

14. $(1.1)^2$

15. 1^{100}

Answer Key

1. 9

2. 8

3. 1

4. 0

5. $\dfrac{1}{8}$

6. 0.0001

7. 16

8. -16

9. -27

10. -27

11. $\dfrac{1}{9}$

12. -0.064

13. -1

14. 1.21

15. 1

Solutions

1. $3^2 = 3 \cdot 3 = 9$

2. $2^3 = 2 \cdot 2 \cdot 2 = 8$

3. $1^5 = 1 \cdot 1 \cdot 1 \cdot 1 \cdot 1 = 1$

4. $0^4 = 0 \cdot 0 \cdot 0 \cdot 0 = 0$

5. $\left(\dfrac{1}{2}\right)^3 = \left(\dfrac{1}{2}\right)\left(\dfrac{1}{2}\right)\left(\dfrac{1}{2}\right) = \dfrac{1}{8}$

6. $(0.1)^4 = (0.1)(0.1)(0.1)(0.1) = 0.0001$

7. $(-2)^4 = (-2)(-2)(-2)(-2) = 16$

8. $-2^4 = -(2)(2)(2)(2) = -16$

9. $(-3)^3 = (-3)(-3)(-3) = -27$

10. $-3^3 = -(3)(3)(3) = -27$

11. $\left(-\dfrac{1}{3}\right)^2 = \left(-\dfrac{1}{3}\right)\left(-\dfrac{1}{3}\right) = \dfrac{1}{9}$

12. $(-0.4)^3 = (-0.4)(-0.4)(-0.4) = -0.064$

13. $-1^6 = -(1)(1)(1)(1)(1)(1) = -1$

14. $(1.1)^2 = (1.1)(1.1) = 1.21$

15. $1^{100} = \underbrace{1 \cdot 1 \cdot 1 \cdot \ldots \cdot 1}_{\text{100 copies}} = 1$

NEGATIVE EXPONENTS

17

Express each of the following using only positive exponents.

1. 2^{-3}

2. 3^{-5}

3. 4^{-2}

4. $\dfrac{1}{3^{-2}}$

5. $\dfrac{1}{5^{-3}}$

6. $\dfrac{1}{7^{-1}}$

7. 1^{-1}

8. 10^{-4}

9. $\dfrac{1}{100^{-2}}$

10. $500,000^{-6}$

11. $2\left(3^{-6}\right)$

12. $4\left(7^{-2}\right)$

13. $\dfrac{5}{2^{-6}}$

14. $\dfrac{7}{4^{-3}}$

15. $\dfrac{7^{-4}}{2^{-3}}$

16. $\dfrac{3^{-5}\cdot 2^{-1}}{5^{-2}}$

17. $\dfrac{6^{-3}\cdot 5^{-4}}{2^{-6}\cdot 10^{-2}}$

18. $9^{-2}\cdot 5^{-6}\cdot 7^{-4}\cdot 2^{5}$

19. $\dfrac{2^{-5}\cdot 6^{-3}\cdot 5^{2}\cdot 7^{-4}}{4^{-2}\cdot 9^{-5}\cdot 11^{3}}$

20. $\dfrac{12^{-2}\cdot 3^{-9}\cdot 5^{-6}\cdot 4^{3}}{7^{2}\cdot 8^{3}\cdot 9^{-4}\cdot 10^{-8}}$

Notes

Notes

1. $2^{-3} = \dfrac{1}{2^3}$

2. $3^{-5} = \dfrac{1}{3^5}$

3. $4^{-2} = \dfrac{1}{4^2}$

4. $\dfrac{1}{3^{-2}} = 3^2$

5. $\dfrac{1}{5^{-3}} = 5^3$

6. $\dfrac{1}{7^{-1}} = 7^1$

7. $1^{-1} = \dfrac{1}{1^1}$

8. $10^{-4} = \dfrac{1}{10^4}$

9. $\dfrac{1}{100^{-2}} = 100^2$

10. $500,000^{-6} = \dfrac{1}{\left(500,000\right)^6}$

11. $2\left(3^{-6}\right) = \dfrac{2}{3^6}$

12. $4\left(7^{-2}\right) = \dfrac{4}{7^2}$

13. $\dfrac{5}{2^{-6}} = 5 \cdot 2^6$

14. $\dfrac{7}{4^{-3}} = 7 \cdot 4^3$

15. $\dfrac{7^{-4}}{2^{-3}} = \dfrac{2^3}{7^4}$

16. $\dfrac{3^{-5} \cdot 2^{-1}}{5^{-2}} = \dfrac{5^2}{3^5 \cdot 2^1}$

17. $\dfrac{6^{-3} \cdot 5^{-4}}{2^{-6} \cdot 10^{-2}} = \dfrac{2^6 \cdot 10^2}{6^3 \cdot 5^4}$

18. $9^{-2} \cdot 5^{-6} \cdot 7^{-4} \cdot 2^5 = \dfrac{2^5}{9^2 \cdot 5^6 \cdot 7^4}$

19. $\dfrac{2^{-5} \cdot 6^{-3} \cdot 5^2 \cdot 7^{-4}}{4^{-2} \cdot 9^{-5} \cdot 11^3} = \dfrac{5^2 \cdot 4^2 \cdot 9^5}{11^3 \cdot 2^5 \cdot 6^3 \cdot 7^4}$

20. $\dfrac{12^{-2} \cdot 3^{-9} \cdot 5^{-6} \cdot 4^3}{7^2 \cdot 8^3 \cdot 9^{-4} \cdot 10^{-8}} = \dfrac{4^3 \cdot 9^4 \cdot 10^8}{7^2 \cdot 8^3 \cdot 12^2 \cdot 3^9 \cdot 5^6}$

FRACTIONAL EXPONENTS

18

Express each of the following radical expressions using a fractional exponent.

1. $\sqrt[3]{2^2}$

6. $\sqrt[4]{81}$

2. $\sqrt[4]{1^3}$

7. $\sqrt[3]{8}$

3. $\sqrt{25}$

8. $\sqrt[5]{32}$

4. $\sqrt{36}$

9. $\sqrt{4^3}$

5. $\sqrt{100}$

10. $\sqrt{\dfrac{1}{3}}$

Express each of the following using radical $\left(\sqrt{}\right)$ notation.

11. $2^{\frac{3}{5}}$

16. $10^{\frac{1}{3}}$

12. $7^{\frac{2}{3}}$

17. $4^{\frac{5}{3}}$

13. $5^{\frac{1}{2}}$

18. $8^{\frac{6}{4}}$

14. $6^{\frac{1}{2}}$

19. $1^{\frac{1}{2}}$

15. $9^{\frac{1}{4}}$

20. $0^{\frac{1}{2}}$

Notes

1. $\sqrt[3]{2^2} = 2^{\frac{2}{3}}$

2. $\sqrt[4]{1^3} = 1^{\frac{3}{4}}$

3. $\sqrt{25} = 25^{\frac{1}{2}}$

4. $\sqrt{36} = 36^{\frac{1}{2}}$

5. $\sqrt{100} = 100^{\frac{1}{2}}$

6. $\sqrt[4]{81} = 81^{\frac{1}{4}}$

7. $\sqrt[3]{8} = 8^{\frac{1}{3}}$

8. $\sqrt[5]{32} = 32^{\frac{1}{5}}$

9. $\sqrt{4^3} = 4^{\frac{3}{2}}$

10. $\sqrt{\frac{1}{3}} = \left(\frac{1}{3}\right)^{\frac{1}{2}}$

11. $2^{\frac{3}{5}} = \sqrt[5]{2^3}$

12. $7^{\frac{2}{3}} = \sqrt[3]{7^2}$

13. $5^{\frac{1}{2}} = \sqrt{5}$

14. $6^{\frac{1}{2}} = \sqrt{6}$

15. $9^{\frac{1}{4}} = \sqrt[4]{9}$

16. $10^{\frac{1}{3}} = \sqrt[3]{10}$

17. $4^{\frac{5}{3}} = \sqrt[3]{4^5}$

18. $8^{\frac{6}{4}} = \sqrt[4]{8^6}$

19. $1^{\frac{1}{2}} = \sqrt{1}$

20. $0^{\frac{1}{2}} = \sqrt{0}$

PROPERTIES OF EXPONENTS

Express each of the following using only a single base and positive exponent.

1. $2^4 \cdot 2^6$

2. $3^4 \cdot 3^2$

3. $5^2 \cdot 5^3 \cdot 5^7$

4. $\dfrac{7^5}{7^2}$

5. $\dfrac{8^6}{8^3}$

6. $\dfrac{5^7}{5}$

7. $\dfrac{3^2 \cdot 3^5}{3^3}$

8. $\dfrac{4^2 \cdot 4^9 \cdot 4^7}{4^8}$

9. $\dfrac{1^2 \cdot 1^3 \cdot 1^{10}}{1^{14}}$

10. $\left(2^3\right)^4$

11. $\left(3^2\right)^7$

12. $\dfrac{\left(4^2\right)^5}{4^3}$

13. $\dfrac{\left(7^3\right)^4}{7^5}$

14. $\dfrac{8^{12}}{\left(8^2\right)^4}$

15. $\dfrac{3^{30}}{\left(3^9\right)^2}$

16. $4^2 \cdot 4^{-5}$

17. $5^{-4} \cdot 5^3 \cdot 5^7$

18. $\dfrac{7^{-5}}{7^2}$

19. $\left(2^{-3}\right)^2$

20. $\left(3^{-4}\right)^6$

Notes

Answer Key

1. 2^{10}

2. 3^6

3. 5^{12}

4. 7^3

5. 8^3

6. 5^6

7. 3^4

8. 4^{10}

9. 1^1

10. 2^{12}

11. 3^{14}

12. 4^7

13. 7^7

14. 8^4

15. 30^{12}

16. $\dfrac{1}{4^3}$

17. 5^6

18. $\dfrac{1}{7^7}$

19. $\dfrac{1}{2^6}$

20. $\dfrac{1}{3^{24}}$

Solutions

1. $2^4 \cdot 2^6 = 2^{4+6} = 2^{10}$

2. $3^4 \cdot 3^2 = 3^{4+2} = 3^6$

3. $5^2 \cdot 5^3 \cdot 5^7 = 5^{2+3+7} = 5^{12}$

4. $\dfrac{7^5}{7^2} = 7^{5-2} = 7^3$

5. $\dfrac{8^6}{8^3} = 8^{6-3} = 8^3$

6. $\dfrac{5^7}{5} = \dfrac{5^7}{5^1} = 5^{7-1} = 5^6$

7. $\dfrac{3^2 \cdot 3^5}{3^3} = 3^{2+5-3} = 3^4$

8. $\dfrac{4^2 \cdot 4^9 \cdot 4^7}{4^8} = 4^{2+9+7-8} = 4^{10}$

9. $\dfrac{1^2 \cdot 1^3 \cdot 1^{10}}{1^{14}} = 1^{2+3+10-14} = 1^1$

10. $\left(2^3\right)^4 = 2^{3(4)} = 2^{12}$

11. $\left(3^2\right)^7 = 3^{2(7)} = 3^{14}$

12. $\dfrac{\left(4^2\right)^5}{4^3} = \dfrac{4^{2(5)}}{4^3} = \dfrac{4^{10}}{4^3} = 4^{10-3} = 4^7$

13. $\dfrac{\left(7^3\right)^4}{7^5} = \dfrac{7^{3(4)}}{7^5} = \dfrac{7^{12}}{7^5} = 7^{12-5} = 7^7$

14. $\dfrac{8^{12}}{\left(8^2\right)^4} = \dfrac{8^{12}}{8^{2(4)}} = \dfrac{8^{12}}{8^8} = 8^{12-8} = 8^4$

15. $\dfrac{3^{30}}{\left(3^9\right)^2} = \dfrac{3^{30}}{3^{9(2)}} = \dfrac{3^{30}}{3^{18}} = 3^{30-18} = 30^{12}$

16. $4^2 \cdot 4^{-5} = 4^{2+(-5)} = 4^{-3} = \dfrac{1}{4^3}$

17. $5^{-4} \cdot 5^3 \cdot 5^7 = 5^{-4+3+7} = 5^6$

18. $\dfrac{7^{-5}}{7^2} = 7^{-5-2} = 7^{-7} = \dfrac{1}{7^7}$

19. $\left(2^{-3}\right)^2 = 2^{-3(2)} = 2^{-6} = \dfrac{1}{2^6}$

20. $\left(3^{-4}\right)^6 = 3^{-4(6)} = 3^{-24} = \dfrac{1}{3^{24}}$

ROOTS AND RADICALS

Calculate each of the following:

1. $\sqrt{25}$

2. $\sqrt{36}$

3. $\sqrt{1}$

4. $\sqrt{0}$

5. $\sqrt[3]{8}$

6. $\sqrt[3]{125}$

7. $\sqrt{64}$

8. $\sqrt[3]{64}$

9. $\sqrt[4]{81}$

10. $\sqrt[5]{32}$

11. $\sqrt[18]{1}$

12. $\sqrt[20]{0}$

13. $\sqrt{100} - \sqrt[3]{27}$

14. $\sqrt{144} + \sqrt[4]{1}$

15. $\sqrt[6]{64} + \sqrt[7]{128}$

Solutions

1. $\sqrt{25} = \pm 5$

2. $\sqrt{36} = \pm 6$

3. $\sqrt{1} = \pm 1$

4. $\sqrt{0} = 0$

5. $\sqrt[3]{8} = 2$

6. $\sqrt[3]{125} = 5$

7. $\sqrt{64} = \pm 8$

8. $\sqrt[3]{64} = 4$

9. $\sqrt[4]{81} = \pm 3$

10. $\sqrt[5]{32} = 2$

11. $\sqrt[18]{1} = \pm 1$

12. $\sqrt[20]{0} = 0$

13. Keeping only the primary (positive) root:
$$\sqrt{100} - \sqrt[3]{27} = 10 - 3 = 7$$

14. Keeping only the primary (positive) root:
$$\sqrt{144} + \sqrt[4]{1} = 12 + 1 = 13$$

15. Keeping only the primary (positive) root:
$$\sqrt[6]{64} + \sqrt[7]{128} = 2 + 2 = 4$$

SCIENTIFIC NOTATION

Express each of the following using scientific notation.

1. $25,800,000,000$

2. $1,379,600,000$

3. 0.000000947

4. 0.000063

Express each of the following scientific notation expressions as a standard number.

5. 2.5×10^6

6. 3.72×10^8

7. 4.9×10^{-4}

8. 1.37×10^{-5}

Calculate the following.

9. $\left(2.9 \times 10^{14}\right)\left(3.6 \times 10^{-5}\right)$

10. $\dfrac{4.72 \times 10^8}{7.53 \times 10^3}$

Notes

Solutions

1. $25,800,000,000 = 2.58 \times 10^{10}$

2. $1,379,600,000 = 1.3796 \times 10^{9}$

3. $0.000000947 = 9.47 \times 10^{-7}$

4. $0.000063 = 6.3 \times 10^{-5}$

5. $2.5 \times 10^{6} = 2,500,000$

6. $3.72 \times 10^{8} = 372,000,000$

7. $4.9 \times 10^{-4} = 0.00049$

8. $1.37 \times 10^{-5} = 0.0000137$

9. $\left(2.9 \times 10^{14}\right)\left(3.6 \times 10^{-5}\right) = 1.0 \times 10^{10}$

10. $\dfrac{4.72 \times 10^{8}}{7.53 \times 10^{3}} = 6.27 \times 10^{4}$

THE ORDER OF OPERATIONS

Simplify each of the following using the correct order of operations.

1. $2(3+7)-1$

2. $3(1-5)+2(7-3)$

3. 3^2-1

4. $4^2-3(5-1)$

5. $2(1+\sqrt{36})$

6. $-2(2^3+3^2)$

7. $-5(\sqrt{49}-\sqrt{25})+3(1^2+2^2)$

8. $\sqrt{3^2+4^2}$

9. $-\left[-(-2)^2-(4-6)^3\right]$

10. $-\sqrt{(4-7)^2+7}$

11. $\dfrac{5^2-1}{7}+3^3$

12. $\left(\sqrt{81}+2\right)^2-\dfrac{1000}{100}$

13. $-2^3\left[\left(1^2-0^3\right)^4+6\right]$

14. $-\left[(-1)^4-2^3+(-3)^2-4^1\right]^2$

15. $\left\{-\left[(-1)^3\right]^2\right\}^4$

Answer Key

1. 19

2. −4

3. 8

4. 4

5. 14

6. −34

7. 5

8. 5

9. −4

10. −4

11. $30\frac{3}{7}$

12. 111

13. −56

14. −4

15. 1

Solutions

1. $2(3+7)-1$

   $2(10)-1$

   $20-1$

   19

2. $3(1-5)+2(7-3)$

   $3(-4)+2(4)$

   $-12+8$

   -4

3. 3^2-1

   $9-1$

   8

4. $4^2-3(5-1)$

   $4^2-3(4)$

   $16-3(4)$

   $16-12$

   4

5. $2(1+\sqrt{36})$

   $2(1+6)$

   $2(7)$

   14

6. $-2(2^3+3^2)$

   $-2(8+9)$

   $-2(17)$

   -34

7. $-5(\sqrt{49}-\sqrt{25})+3(1^2+2^2)$

   $-5(7-5)+3(1+4)$

   $-5(2)+3(5)$

   $-10+15$

   5

8. $\sqrt{3^2+4^2}$

   $\sqrt{9+16}$

   $\sqrt{25}$

   5

9. $-\left[-(-2)^2-(4-6)^3\right]$

   $-\left[-(-2)^2-(-2)^3\right]$

   $-\left[-(4)-(-8)\right]$

   $-[-4+8]$

   $-[4]$

   -4

10. $-\sqrt{(4-7)^2+7}$

    $-\sqrt{(-3)^2+7}$

    $-\sqrt{9+7}$

    $-\sqrt{16}$

    -4

Notes

11. $\dfrac{5^2-1}{7}+3^3$

$\dfrac{25-1}{7}+27$

$\dfrac{24}{7}+27$

$3\dfrac{3}{7}+27$

$30\dfrac{3}{7}$

12. $\left(\sqrt{81}+2\right)^2-\dfrac{1000}{100}$

$(9+2)^2-\dfrac{1000}{100}$

$(11)^2-\dfrac{1000}{100}$

$121-\dfrac{1000}{100}$

$121-10$

111

13. $-2^3\left[\left(1^2-0^3\right)^4+6\right]$

$-2^3\left[(1-0)^4+6\right]$

$-2^3\left[(1)^4+6\right]$

$-2^3[1+6]$

$-2^3[7]$

$-8[7]$

-56

14. $-\left[(-1)^4-2^3+(-3)^2-4^1\right]^2$

$-[1-8+9-4]^2$

$-[-2]^2$

$-(4)$

-4

15. $\left\{-\left[(-1)^3\right]^2\right\}^4$

$\left\{-[-1]^2\right\}^4$

$\left\{-(1)\right\}^4$

$\left\{-1\right\}^4$

1

Sets, Subsets, and Elements

Insert the appropriate symbol $(\in, \notin, \subset, \not\subset)$ into each of the following expressions.

1. $4\,\square\,\{1, 2, 3, 4, 5\}$

2. $\{a, b\}\,\square\,\{a, b, c, d, e, f, g\}$

3. $7\,\square\,\{1, 2, 3\}$

4. $\{1, 3, 5\}\,\square\,\{1, 2, 3, 4\}$

5. $\{\text{all positive real numbers}\}\,\square\,\{\text{all real numbers}\}$

6. $5\,\square\,\{\text{all even numbers}\}$

7. $\dfrac{1}{4}\,\square\,\{\text{all rational numbers}\}$

8. $-6.5\,\square\,\{\text{all real numbers greater than} -6\}$

9. $\{\text{real numbers between } 0 \text{ and } 1\}\,\square\,\{\text{all real numbers}\}$

10. $\{\text{the letters in the word "mathematics"}\}\,\square\,\{\text{the first } 24 \text{ letters in the alphabet}\}$

Notes

Solutions

1. $4 \boxed{\in} \{1, 2, 3, 4, 5\}$

2. $\{a, b\} \boxed{\subset} \{a, b, c, d, e, f, g\}$

3. $7 \boxed{\notin} \{1, 2, 3\}$

4. $\{1, 3, 5\} \boxed{\not\subset} \{1, 2, 3, 4\}$

5. $\{\text{all positive real numbers}\} \boxed{\subset} \{\text{all real numbers}\}$

6. $5 \boxed{\notin} \{\text{all even numbers}\}$

7. $\dfrac{1}{4} \boxed{\in} \{\text{all rational numbers}\}$

8. $-6.5 \boxed{\notin} \{\text{all real numbers greater than } -6\}$

9. $\{\text{real numbers between } 0 \text{ and } 1\} \boxed{\subset} \{\text{all real numbers}\}$

10. $\{\text{the letters in the word "mathematics"}\} \boxed{\not\subset} \{\text{the first 24 letters in the alphabet}\}$

THE INTERSECTION AND UNION OF SETS

Find each of the following.

1. $\{1, 2, 3\} \cup \{4, 5, 6\}$

2. $\{1, 2, 3\} \cap \{2, 3, 4\}$

3. $\{-1, 2, 5, 8\} \cup \{2, 3, 4, 5\}$

4. $\{-3, -2, -1\} \cup \{a, b\}$

5. $\{2, 4, 6, 8\} \cap \{1, 3, 5, 7\}$

6. $\{1, 2, 3\} \cup \left(\{3, 4, 5, 6\} \cap \{5, 6, 7\}\right)$

7. $\{\text{all positive real numbers}\} \cap \{\text{all real numbers}\}$

8. $\{\text{all even numbers}\} \cap \{\text{all odd numbers}\}$

9. $\{\text{all real numbers greater than zero}\} \cap \{\text{all real numbers less than } 25\}$

10. $\{0\} \cup \{\text{all real numbers greater than zero}\}$

Solutions

1. $\{1, 2, 3\} \cup \{4, 5, 6\} = \{1, 2, 3, 4, 5, 6\}$

2. $\{1, 2, 3\} \cap \{2, 3, 4\} = \{2, 3\}$

3. $\{-1, 2, 5, 8\} \cup \{2, 3, 4, 5\} = \{-1, 2, 3, 4, 5, 8\}$

4. $\{-3, -2, -1\} \cup \{a, b\} = \{-3, -2, -1, a, b\}$

5. $\{2, 4, 6, 8\} \cap \{1, 3, 5, 7\} = \varnothing$

6. $\{1, 2, 3\} \cup (\{3, 4, 5, 6\} \cap \{5, 6, 7\})$

    $= \{1, 2, 3\} \cup \{5, 6\}$

    $= \{1, 2, 3, 5, 6\}$

7. $\{\text{all positive real numbers}\} \cap \{\text{all real numbers}\}$

    $= \{\text{all positive real numbers}\}$

8. $\{\text{all even numbers}\} \cap \{\text{all odd numbers}\} = \varnothing$

9. $\{\text{all real numbers greater than zero}\} \cap \{\text{all real numbers less than } 25\}$

    $= \{\text{all real numbers greater than zero and less than } 25\}$

10. $\{0\} \cup \{\text{all real numbers greater than zero}\}$

    $= \{\text{all real numbers greater than or equal to zero}\}$

ABSOLUTE VALUE

Find each of the following absolute values.

Notes

1. $|5| =$

2. $|-5| =$

3. $|12| =$

4. $|-12| =$

5. $\left|\dfrac{2}{5}\right| =$

6. $\left|-\dfrac{2}{5}\right| =$

7. $|3.8| =$

8. $|-3.8| =$

9. $|2-5| =$

10. $|6+9| =$

11. $|3(1)-5(2)| =$

12. $|-2(8-12)| =$

13. $|3(4+8)-2(18)| =$

14. $\left|\dfrac{2-5}{6}\right| =$

15. $\left|-\left\{-\left[-(6-7)\right]\right\}\right| =$

Notes

Answer Key

1. 5

2. 5

3. 12

4. 12

5. $\dfrac{2}{5}$

6. $\dfrac{2}{5}$

7. 3.8

8. 3.8

9. 3

10. 15

11. 7

12. 8

13. 0

14. $\dfrac{1}{2}$

15. 1

Solutions

1. $|5| = 5$

2. $|-5| = 5$

3. $|12| = 12$

4. $|-12| = 12$

5. $\left|\dfrac{2}{5}\right| = \dfrac{2}{5}$

6. $\left|-\dfrac{2}{5}\right| = \dfrac{2}{5}$

7. $|3.8| = 3.8$

8. $|-3.8| = 3.8$

9. $|2-5| = |-3| = 3$

10. $|6+9| = |15| = 15$

11. $|3(1)-5(2)| = |3-10| = |-7| = 7$

12. $|-2(8-12)| = |-2(-4)| = |8| = 8$

13. $|3(4+8)-2(18)| = |3(12)-36| = |36-36| = |0| = 0$

14. $\left|\dfrac{2-5}{6}\right| = \left|\dfrac{-3}{6}\right| = \left|-\dfrac{1}{2}\right| = \dfrac{1}{2}$

15. $\left|-\left\{-\left[-(6-7)\right]\right\}\right| = \left|-\left\{-\left[-(-1)\right]\right\}\right| = \left|-\left\{-\left[\,1\,\right]\right\}\right| = \left|-\left\{-1\right\}\right| = |1| = 1$

Simplifying
Algebraic Expressions

Simplify each of the following algebraic expressions.

Notes

1. $3x + 2x$

2. $9b - 2b$

3. $\dfrac{1}{2}a + a$

4. $3\dfrac{1}{2}x + 6\dfrac{1}{2}x$

5. $8t + 2t - 5t$

6. $4\dfrac{1}{2}x - x + 2\dfrac{1}{2}x$

7. $5x - 3y + 7x$

8. $18b - 9k - 13b$

9. $2(15x)$

10. $5(2c)$

11. $8k + 3(4k) + 6(5p)$

12. $\dfrac{1}{3}x + \dfrac{1}{2}x$

13. $3.2a + 5.7a$

14. $2\dfrac{1}{5}t + 3\dfrac{1}{3}t$

15. $\dfrac{1}{4}\left(\dfrac{1}{3}x\right) + \dfrac{1}{3}\left(\dfrac{1}{2}x\right)$

16. $\dfrac{1}{2}x + 0.5x$

17. $\dfrac{1}{3}x + 0.5x$

18. $2.5(2x) + 7\left(\dfrac{1}{7}x\right)$

19. $3.5d + (4.5 - 6)d + 2.6R$

20. $(3 - 6 - 12)x - 2x - (-4x)$

Answer Key

1. $5x$

2. $7b$

3. $1\frac{1}{2}a$

4. $10x$

5. $5t$

6. $6x$

7. $12x - 3y$

8. $5b - 9k$

9. $30x$

10. $10c$

11. $20k + 30p$

12. $\frac{5}{6}x$

13. $8.9a$

14. $5\frac{8}{15}t$

15. $\frac{1}{4}x$

16. x

17. $\frac{5}{6}x$

18. $6x$

19. $2d + 2.6R$

20. $-13x$

Solutions

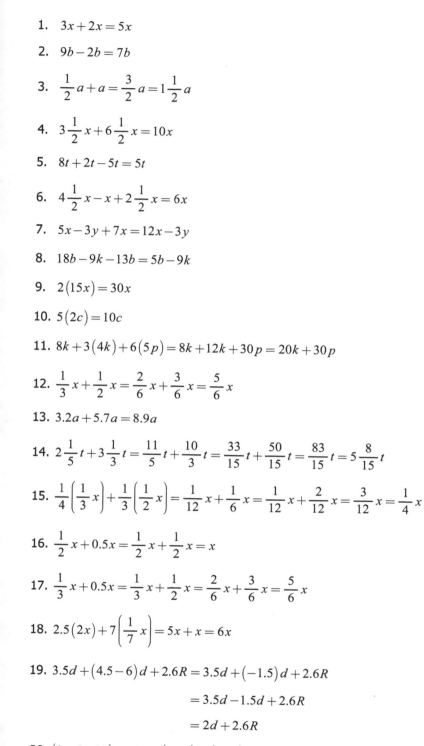

1. $3x + 2x = 5x$

2. $9b - 2b = 7b$

3. $\dfrac{1}{2}a + a = \dfrac{3}{2}a = 1\dfrac{1}{2}a$

4. $3\dfrac{1}{2}x + 6\dfrac{1}{2}x = 10x$

5. $8t + 2t - 5t = 5t$

6. $4\dfrac{1}{2}x - x + 2\dfrac{1}{2}x = 6x$

7. $5x - 3y + 7x = 12x - 3y$

8. $18b - 9k - 13b = 5b - 9k$

9. $2(15x) = 30x$

10. $5(2c) = 10c$

11. $8k + 3(4k) + 6(5p) = 8k + 12k + 30p = 20k + 30p$

12. $\dfrac{1}{3}x + \dfrac{1}{2}x = \dfrac{2}{6}x + \dfrac{3}{6}x = \dfrac{5}{6}x$

13. $3.2a + 5.7a = 8.9a$

14. $2\dfrac{1}{5}t + 3\dfrac{1}{3}t = \dfrac{11}{5}t + \dfrac{10}{3}t = \dfrac{33}{15}t + \dfrac{50}{15}t = \dfrac{83}{15}t = 5\dfrac{8}{15}t$

15. $\dfrac{1}{4}\left(\dfrac{1}{3}x\right) + \dfrac{1}{3}\left(\dfrac{1}{2}x\right) = \dfrac{1}{12}x + \dfrac{1}{6}x = \dfrac{1}{12}x + \dfrac{2}{12}x = \dfrac{3}{12}x = \dfrac{1}{4}x$

16. $\dfrac{1}{2}x + 0.5x = \dfrac{1}{2}x + \dfrac{1}{2}x = x$

17. $\dfrac{1}{3}x + 0.5x = \dfrac{1}{3}x + \dfrac{1}{2}x = \dfrac{2}{6}x + \dfrac{3}{6}x = \dfrac{5}{6}x$

18. $2.5(2x) + 7\left(\dfrac{1}{7}x\right) = 5x + x = 6x$

19. $3.5d + (4.5 - 6)d + 2.6R = 3.5d + (-1.5)d + 2.6R$

$$= 3.5d - 1.5d + 2.6R$$

$$= 2d + 2.6R$$

20. $(3 - 6 - 12)x - 2x - (-4x) = (-15)x - 2x + 4x = -15x - 2x + 4x = -13x$

ADDING AND SUBTRACTING POLYNOMIALS

Add/subtract the following polynomials.

1. $(3x+5)+(2x-1)=$

2. $(7x^2+4x+6)+(3x^2-x-5)=$

3. $(10x+8)-(6x+3)=$

4. $(15x^2+9x-8)-(12x^2-7x+6)=$

5. $(x^3+5x+1)+(6x^2+8)=$

6. $(6x^4-9x^2)-(7x^4-10x^3+x^2+2)=$

7. $(-4x^3+8)+(7x^3+5x^2-9x-1)=$

8. $(5x^3-7x+10)-(-x^4-x^3-x^2-x)=$

9. $\left(\dfrac{1}{2}x^3+\dfrac{3}{4}x^2-\dfrac{1}{8}\right)+\left(\dfrac{1}{2}x^2+\dfrac{1}{5}x+\dfrac{3}{4}\right)=$

10. $\left(\dfrac{2}{3}x^4-\dfrac{1}{6}x^3+x\right)-\left(\dfrac{1}{9}x^4-\dfrac{1}{8}x^2+\dfrac{1}{5}x+5\right)=$

11. $(1.2x^2+3.7x-0.7)+(2.3x^3-3.1x^2+5.8x)=$

12. $(12.25x^3-1.95x^2+2.8)-(3.28x^2+0.91x)=$

13. $(7x^2-8)-(4x^3-3x^2-2)+(5x^4-9x^3-6x^2)=$

14. $2(x^3+4)-8(x^2+2x+1)=$

15. $4\left(\dfrac{1}{8}x^3-\dfrac{1}{2}x^2+1\right)+3\left(\dfrac{1}{6}x^2+\dfrac{1}{3}x-2\right)+2(1.5x^4+0.5x^3+2.5)=$

Answer Key

1. $5x + 4$

2. $10x^2 + 3x + 1$

3. $4x + 5$

4. $3x^2 + 16x - 14$

5. $x^3 + 6x^2 + 5x + 9$

6. $-x^4 + 10x^3 - 10x^2 - 2$

7. $3x^3 + 5x^2 - 9x + 7$

8. $x^4 + 6x^3 + x^2 - 6x + 10$

9. $\frac{1}{2}x^3 + 1\frac{1}{4}x^2 + \frac{1}{5}x + \frac{5}{8}$

10. $\frac{5}{9}x^4 - \frac{1}{6}x^3 + \frac{1}{8}x^2 + \frac{4}{5}x - 5$

11. $2.3x^3 - 1.9x^2 + 9.5x - 0.7$

12. $12.25x^3 - 5.23x^2 - 0.91x + 2.8$

13. $5x^4 - 13x^3 + 4x^2 - 6$

14. $2x^3 - 8x^2 - 16x$

15. $3x^4 + 1\frac{1}{2}x^3 - 1\frac{1}{2}x^2 + x + 3$

Solutions

1. $(3x+5)+(2x-1) = 3x+5+2x-1$

   $= 5x+4$

2. $(7x^2+4x+6)+(3x^2-x-5) = 7x^2+4x+6+3x^2-x-5$

   $= 10x^2+3x+1$

3. $(10x+8)-(6x+3) = 10x+8-6x-3$

   $= 4x+5$

4. $(15x^2+9x-8)-(12x^2-7x+6) = 15x^2+9x-8-12x^2+7x-6$

   $= 3x^2+16x-14$

5. $(x^3+5x+1)+(6x^2+8) = x^3+5x+1+6x^2+8$

   $= x^3+6x^2+5x+9$

6. $(6x^4-9x^2)-(7x^4-10x^3+x^2+2) = 6x^4-9x^2-7x^4+10x^3-x^2-2$

   $= -x^4+10x^3-10x^2-2$

7. $(-4x^3+8)+(7x^3+5x^2-9x-1) = -4x^3+8+7x^3+5x^2-9x-1$

   $= 3x^3+5x^2-9x+7$

8. $(5x^3-7x+10)-(-x^4-x^3-x^2-x) = 5x^3-7x+10+x^4+x^3+x^2+x$

   $= x^4+6x^3+x^2-6x+10$

9. $\left(\dfrac{1}{2}x^3+\dfrac{3}{4}x^2-\dfrac{1}{8}\right)+\left(\dfrac{1}{2}x^2+\dfrac{1}{5}x+\dfrac{3}{4}\right) = \dfrac{1}{2}x^3+\dfrac{3}{4}x^2-\dfrac{1}{8}+\dfrac{1}{2}x^2+\dfrac{1}{5}x+\dfrac{3}{4}$

   $= \dfrac{1}{2}x^3+\dfrac{3}{4}x^2+\dfrac{1}{2}x^2+\dfrac{1}{5}x-\dfrac{1}{8}+\dfrac{3}{4}$

   $= \dfrac{1}{2}x^3+\dfrac{3}{4}x^2+\dfrac{2}{4}x^2+\dfrac{1}{5}x-\dfrac{1}{8}+\dfrac{6}{8}$

   $= \dfrac{1}{2}x^3+\dfrac{5}{4}x^2+\dfrac{1}{5}x+\dfrac{5}{8}$

   $= \dfrac{1}{2}x^3+1\dfrac{1}{4}x^2+\dfrac{1}{5}x+\dfrac{5}{8}$

10. $\left(\dfrac{2}{3}x^4 - \dfrac{1}{6}x^3 + x\right) - \left(\dfrac{1}{9}x^4 - \dfrac{1}{8}x^2 + \dfrac{1}{5}x + 5\right) = \dfrac{2}{3}x^4 - \dfrac{1}{6}x^3 + x - \dfrac{1}{9}x^4 + \dfrac{1}{8}x^2 - \dfrac{1}{5}x - 5$

$$= \dfrac{2}{3}x^4 - \dfrac{1}{9}x^4 - \dfrac{1}{6}x^3 + \dfrac{1}{8}x^2 + x - \dfrac{1}{5}x - 5$$

$$= \dfrac{6}{9}x^4 - \dfrac{1}{9}x^4 - \dfrac{1}{6}x^3 + \dfrac{1}{8}x^2 + x - \dfrac{1}{5}x - 5$$

$$= \dfrac{5}{9}x^4 - \dfrac{1}{6}x^3 + \dfrac{1}{8}x^2 + \dfrac{4}{5}x - 5$$

11. $\left(1.2x^2 + 3.7x - 0.7\right) + \left(2.3x^3 - 3.1x^2 + 5.8x\right) = 1.2x^2 + 3.7x - 0.7 + 2.3x^3 - 3.1x^2 + 5.8x$

$$= 2.3x^3 - 1.9x^2 + 9.5x - 0.7$$

12. $\left(12.25x^3 - 1.95x^2 + 2.8\right) - \left(3.28x^2 + 0.91x\right) = 12.25x^3 - 1.95x^2 + 2.8 - 3.28x^2 - 0.91x$

$$= 12.25x^3 - 5.23x^2 - 0.91x + 2.8$$

13. $\left(7x^2 - 8\right) - \left(4x^3 - 3x^2 - 2\right) + \left(5x^4 - 9x^3 - 6x^2\right) = 7x^2 - 8 - 4x^3 + 3x^2 + 2 + 5x^4 - 9x^3 - 6x^2$

$$= 5x^4 - 13x^3 + 4x^2 - 6$$

14. $2\left(x^3 + 4\right) - 8\left(x^2 + 2x + 1\right) = 2\left(x^3\right) + 2\left(4\right) + \left(-8\right)\left(x^2\right) + \left(-8\right)\left(2x\right) + \left(-8\right)\left(1\right)$

$$= 2x^3 + 8 - 8x^2 - 16x - 8$$

$$= 2x^3 - 8x^2 - 16x$$

15. $4\left(\dfrac{1}{8}x^3 - \dfrac{1}{2}x^2 + 1\right) + 3\left(\dfrac{1}{6}x^2 + \dfrac{1}{3}x - 2\right) + 2\left(1.5x^4 + 0.5x^3 + 2.5\right)$

$$= 4\left(\dfrac{1}{8}x^3\right) + 4\left(-\dfrac{1}{2}x^2\right) + 4\left(1\right) + 3\left(\dfrac{1}{6}x^2\right) + 3\left(\dfrac{1}{3}x\right) + 3\left(-2\right) + 2\left(1.5x^4\right) + 2\left(0.5x^3\right) + 2\left(2.5\right)$$

$$= \dfrac{1}{2}x^3 - 2x^2 + 4 + \dfrac{1}{2}x^2 + x - 6 + 3x^4 + x^3 + 5$$

$$= 3x^4 + \dfrac{3}{2}x^3 - \dfrac{3}{2}x^2 + x + 3$$

$$= 3x^4 + 1\dfrac{1}{2}x^3 - 1\dfrac{1}{2}x^2 + x + 3$$

SOLVING EQUATIONS

Solve each of the following equations.

1. $x + 2 = 7$

2. $x - 3 = 10$

3. $x + \dfrac{1}{2} = 6$

4. $2x = 8$

5. $6x = 1$

6. $\dfrac{x}{5} = 3$

7. $\dfrac{x}{7} = 2$

8. $2x - 1 = 13$

9. $6x + 1 = 25$

10. $\dfrac{x+2}{3} = 6$

11. $\dfrac{x-1}{2} = 5$

12. $3(x-1) = 15$

13. $2(x+6) = 20$

14. $\dfrac{1}{5}(x-1) = 8$

15. $\dfrac{1}{2}\left(x + \dfrac{1}{4}\right) = 6$

16. $2(x-1) + 7 = 8$

17. $4(x+1) + 3(x+5) = 20$

18. $0.5x + 3.5 = 5.5$

19. $2.5x - \dfrac{3}{4} = 1.75$

20. $\dfrac{2}{x} = 10$

21. $\dfrac{4}{x} = 12$

22. $\dfrac{3}{x+1} = 1$

23. $\dfrac{5}{x-7} = 2$

24. $x + 4 = -x - 6$

25. $3 + \dfrac{1}{x-1} = 2$

26. $x - 2 = 3x + 1$

27. $\dfrac{3}{4}x + 7 = 0.5x - 8$

28. $\dfrac{1}{2(x-1)} + 1 = 7.5$

29. $\dfrac{2.5x}{7.5} + 1 = 0.5$

30. $6(x+2) - 4(x-1) = 3(x+5) + 2(3-x)$

Notes

Answer Key

1. $x = 5$

2. $x = 13$

3. $x = 5\frac{1}{2}$

4. $x = 4$

5. $x = \frac{1}{6}$

6. $x = 15$

7. $x = 14$

8. $x = 7$

9. $x = 4$

10. $x = 16$

11. $x = 11$

12. $x = 6$

13. $x = 4$

14. $x = 41$

15. $x = 11\frac{3}{4}$

16. $x = 1\frac{1}{2}$

17. $x = \frac{1}{7}$

18. $x = 4.0$

19. $x = 1.0$

20. $x = \frac{1}{5}$

21. $x = \frac{1}{3}$

22. $x = 2$

23. $x = 9\frac{1}{2}$

24. $x = -5$

25. $x = 0$

26. $x = -1\frac{1}{2}$

27. $x = -60$

28. $x = 1\frac{1}{13}$

29. $x = -1\frac{1}{2}$

30. $x = 5$

Solutions

1. $x + 2 = 7$

$x + 2 - 2 = 7 - 2$

$x = 5$

2. $x - 3 = 10$

$x - 3 + 3 = 10 + 3$

$x = 13$

3. $x + \dfrac{1}{2} = 6$

$x + \dfrac{1}{2} - \dfrac{1}{2} = 6 - \dfrac{1}{2}$

$x = 5\dfrac{1}{2}$

4. $2x = 8$

$\dfrac{2x}{2} = \dfrac{8}{2}$

$x = 4$

5. $6x = 1$

$\dfrac{6x}{6} = \dfrac{1}{6}$

$x = \dfrac{1}{6}$

6. $\dfrac{x}{5} = 3$

$\dfrac{x}{5}(5) = 3(5)$

$x = 15$

7. $\dfrac{x}{7} = 2$

$\dfrac{x}{7}(7) = 2(7)$

$x = 14$

8. $2x - 1 = 13$

$2x - 1 + 1 = 13 + 1$

$2x = 14$

$\dfrac{2x}{2} = \dfrac{14}{2}$

$x = 7$

9. $6x + 1 = 25$

$6x + 1 - 1 = 25 - 1$

$6x = 24$

$\dfrac{6x}{6} = \dfrac{24}{6}$

$x = 4$

10. $\dfrac{x + 2}{3} = 6$

$\dfrac{x + 2}{3}(3) = 6(3)$

$x + 2 = 18$

$x + 2 - 2 = 18 - 2$

$x = 16$

11. $\dfrac{x - 1}{2} = 5$

$\dfrac{x - 1}{2}(2) = 5(2)$

$x - 1 = 10$

$x - 1 + 1 = 10 + 1$

$x = 11$

12. $3(x - 1) = 15$

$\dfrac{3(x - 1)}{3} = \dfrac{15}{3}$

$x - 1 = 5$

$x - 1 + 1 = 5 + 1$

$x = 6$

Notes

13. $2(x+6)=20$

$$\frac{2(x+6)}{2}=\frac{20}{2}$$

$$x+6=10$$

$$x+6-6=10-6$$

$$x=4$$

14. $\frac{1}{5}(x-1)=8$

$$\frac{\frac{1}{5}(x-1)}{\frac{1}{5}}=\frac{8}{\frac{1}{5}}$$

$$x-1=40$$

$$x-1+1=40+1$$

$$x=41$$

15. $\frac{1}{2}\left(x+\frac{1}{4}\right)=6$

$$\frac{\frac{1}{2}\left(x+\frac{1}{4}\right)}{\frac{1}{2}}=\frac{6}{\frac{1}{2}}$$

$$x+\frac{1}{4}-\frac{1}{4}=12-\frac{1}{4}$$

$$x=11\frac{3}{4}$$

16. $2(x-1)+7=8$

$$2(x-1)+7-7=8-7$$

$$2(x-1)=1$$

$$\frac{2(x-1)}{2}=\frac{1}{2}$$

$$x-1=\frac{1}{2}$$

$$x-1+1=\frac{1}{2}+1$$

$$x=1\frac{1}{2}$$

17. $4(x+1)+3(x+5)=20$

$$4x+4+3x+15=20$$

$$7x+19=20$$

$$7x+19-19=20-19$$

$$7x=1$$

$$\frac{7x}{7}=\frac{1}{7}$$

$$x=\frac{1}{7}$$

18. $0.5x+3.5=5.5$

$$0.5x+3.5-3.5=5.5-3.5$$

$$0.5x=2.0$$

$$\frac{0.5x}{0.5}=\frac{2.0}{0.5}$$

$$x=4.0$$

19. $2.5x-\frac{3}{4}=1.75$

$$2.5x-0.75=1.75$$

$$2.5x-0.75+0.75=1.75+0.75$$

$$2.5x=2.5$$

$$\frac{2.5x}{2.5}=\frac{2.5}{2.5}$$

$$x=1.0$$

20. $\frac{2}{x}=10$

$$\frac{2}{x}(x)=10(x)$$

$$2=10x$$

$$\frac{2}{10}=\frac{10x}{10}$$

$$\frac{1}{5}=x$$

$$x=\frac{1}{5}$$

21. $\dfrac{4}{x} = 12$

$\dfrac{4}{x}(x) = 12(x)$

$4 = 12x$

$\dfrac{4}{12} = \dfrac{12x}{12}$

$\dfrac{1}{3} = x$

$x = \dfrac{1}{3}$

22. $\dfrac{3}{x+1} = 1$

$\dfrac{3}{x+1}(x+1) = 1(x+1)$

$3 = x + 1$

$3 - 1 = x + 1 - 1$

$2 = x$

$x = 2$

23. $\dfrac{5}{x-7} = 2$

$\dfrac{5}{x-7}(x-7) = 2(x-7)$

$5 = 2x - 14$

$5 + 14 = 2x - 14 + 14$

$19 = 2x$

$\dfrac{19}{2} = \dfrac{2x}{2}$

$9\dfrac{1}{2} = x$

$x = 9\dfrac{1}{2}$

24. $x + 4 = -x - 6$

$x + 4 + x = -x - 6 + x$

$2x + 4 = -6$

$2x + 4 - 4 = -6 - 4$

$2x = -10$

$\dfrac{2x}{2} = \dfrac{-10}{2}$

$x = -5$

25. $3 + \dfrac{1}{x-1} = 2$

$3 + \dfrac{1}{x-1} - 3 = 2 - 3$

$\dfrac{1}{x-1} = -1$

$\dfrac{1}{x-1}(x-1) = -1(x-1)$

$1 = -1(x-1)$

$1 = -x + 1$

$1 - 1 = -x + 1 - 1$

$0 = -x$

$x = 0$

26. $x - 2 = 3x + 1$

$x - 2 - x = 3x + 1 - x$

$-2 = 2x + 1$

$-2 - 1 = 2x + 1 - 1$

$-3 = 2x$

$\dfrac{-3}{2} = \dfrac{2x}{2}$

$\dfrac{-3}{2} = x$

$x = -1\dfrac{1}{2}$

27. $\dfrac{3}{4}x + 7 = 0.5x - 8$

$\dfrac{3}{4}x + 7 = \dfrac{1}{2}x - 8$

$\dfrac{3}{4}x + 7 - \dfrac{1}{2}x = \dfrac{1}{2}x - 8 - \dfrac{1}{2}x$

$\dfrac{1}{4}x + 7 = -8$

$\dfrac{1}{4}x + 7 - 7 = -8 - 7$

$\dfrac{1}{4}x = -15$

$\dfrac{\dfrac{1}{4}x}{\dfrac{1}{4}} = \dfrac{-15}{\dfrac{1}{4}}$

$x = -60$

28. $\dfrac{1}{2(x-1)} + 1 = 7.5$

$\dfrac{1}{2(x-1)} + 1 - 1 = 7.5 - 1$

$\dfrac{1}{2(x-1)} = 6.5$

$\dfrac{1}{2(x-1)}(x-1) = 6.5(x-1)$

$\dfrac{1}{2} = 6.5x - 6.5$

$\dfrac{1}{2} = \dfrac{13}{2}x - \dfrac{13}{2}$

$\dfrac{1}{2} + \dfrac{13}{2} = \dfrac{13}{2}x - \dfrac{13}{2} + \dfrac{13}{2}$

$\dfrac{14}{2} = \dfrac{13}{2}x$

$7 = \dfrac{13}{2}x$

$2(7) = 2\left(\dfrac{13}{2}x\right)$

$14 = 13x$

$\dfrac{14}{13} = \dfrac{13x}{13}$

$1\dfrac{1}{13} = x$

$x = 1\dfrac{1}{13}$

29. $\dfrac{2.5x}{7.5} + 1 = 0.5$

$$\dfrac{x}{3} + 1 = \dfrac{1}{2}$$

$$\dfrac{x}{3} + 1 - 1 = \dfrac{1}{2} - 1$$

$$\dfrac{x}{3} = -\dfrac{1}{2}$$

$$\dfrac{x}{3}(3) = \left(-\dfrac{1}{2}\right)(3)$$

$$x = -\dfrac{3}{2}$$

$$x = -1\dfrac{1}{2}$$

30. $6(x+2) - 4(x-1) = 3(x+5) + 2(3-x)$

$$6x + 12 - 4x + 4 = 3x + 15 + 6 - 2x$$

$$2x + 16 = x + 21$$

$$2x + 16 - x = x + 21 - x$$

$$x + 16 = 21$$

$$x + 16 - 16 = 21 - 16$$

$$x = 5$$

For each of the following, decide if the ordered pair is a solution of the given equation.

1. $y = x + 3$ $\qquad$ $(1, 4)$

2. $y = x - 2$ $\qquad$ $(3, 1)$

3. $y = x + 5$ $\qquad$ $(2, 8)$

4. $y = 3x + 4$ $\qquad$ $(-4, -8)$

5. $y = \dfrac{1}{2}(x - 6)$ $\qquad$ $(10, 2)$

6. $y = \dfrac{2}{3}(x + 5)$ $\qquad$ $(1, 5)$

7. $y = 3x + 2(x - 1)$ $\qquad$ $(-2, 5)$

8. $y - 6 = 9x$ $\qquad$ $(2, 24)$

9. $3y = 2(x + 5)$ $\qquad$ $(-5, 6)$

10. $\dfrac{y}{2} = \dfrac{x - 2}{3}$ $\qquad$ $(8, 4)$

11. $y + 2x = 5$ $\qquad$ $(9, -2)$

12. $2y - 2(x - 1) = 8$ $\qquad$ $(1, 4)$

13. $2(y + 3) - 3(x - 1) = 4(y - 2)$ $\qquad$ $(2, 6)$

14. $7y - 5(x + 3) = 12$ $\qquad$ $\left(-1, \dfrac{22}{7}\right)$

15. $\dfrac{y - x}{2} - 3.5 = 1$ $\qquad$ $(2, 11)$

Notes

Answer Key

1. yes
2. yes
3. no
4. yes
5. yes
6. no
7. no
8. yes
9. no
10. yes
11. no
12. yes
13. no
14. yes
15. yes

Solutions

1. $y = x + 3$

   $4 \overset{?}{=} 1 + 3$

   $4 = 4$ ✓

   Yes, the ordered pair is a solution.

2. $y = x - 2$

   $1 \overset{?}{=} 3 - 2$

   $1 = 1$ ✓

   Yes, the ordered pair is a solution.

3. $y = x + 5$

   $8 \overset{?}{=} 2 + 5$

   $8 \neq 7$ ✗

   No, the ordered pair is not a solution.

4. $y = 3x + 4$

   $-8 \overset{?}{=} 3(-4) + 4$

   $-8 \overset{?}{=} -12 + 4$

   $-8 = -8$ ✓

   Yes, the ordered pair is a solution.

5. $y = \dfrac{1}{2}(x - 6)$

   $2 \overset{?}{=} \dfrac{1}{2}(10 - 6)$

   $2 \overset{?}{=} \dfrac{1}{2}(4)$

   $2 = 2$ ✓

   Yes, the ordered pair is a solution.

6. $y = \dfrac{2}{3}(x + 5)$

   $5 \overset{?}{=} \dfrac{2}{3}(1 + 5)$

   $5 \overset{?}{=} \dfrac{2}{3}(6)$

   $5 \neq 4$ ✗

   No, the ordered pair is not a solution.

Notes

7. $y = 3x + 2(x - 1)$

$$5 \overset{?}{=} 3(-2) + 2(-2 - 1)$$

$$5 \overset{?}{=} -6 + 2(-3)$$

$$5 \overset{?}{=} -6 - 6$$

$$5 \neq -12 \quad \textbf{✗}$$

No, the ordered pair is not a solution.

8. $y - 6 = 9x$

$$24 - 6 \overset{?}{=} 9(2)$$

$$18 = 18 \quad \checkmark$$

Yes, the ordered pair is a solution.

9. $3y = 2(x + 5)$

$$3(6) \overset{?}{=} 2(-5 + 5)$$

$$18 \overset{?}{=} 2(0)$$

$$18 \neq 0 \quad \textbf{✗}$$

No, the ordered pair is not a solution.

10. $\dfrac{y}{2} = \dfrac{x - 2}{3}$

$$\frac{4}{2} \overset{?}{=} \frac{8 - 2}{3}$$

$$2 \overset{?}{=} \frac{6}{3}$$

$$2 = 2 \quad \checkmark$$

Yes, the ordered pair is a solution.

11. $y + 2x = 5$

$$-2 + 2(9) \overset{?}{=} 5$$

$$-2 + 18 \overset{?}{=} 5$$

$$16 \neq 5 \quad \textbf{✗}$$

No, the ordered pair is not a solution.

12. $2y - 2(x - 1) = 8$

$$2(4) - 2(1 - 1) \overset{?}{=} 8$$

$$8 - 2(0) \overset{?}{=} 8$$

$$8 - 0 \overset{?}{=} 8$$

$$8 = 8 \quad \checkmark$$

Yes, the ordered pair is a solution.

13. $2(y+3)-3(x-1)=4(y-2)$

$2(6+3)-3(2-1)\overset{?}{=}4(6-2)$

$2(9)-3(1)\overset{?}{=}4(4)$

$18-3\overset{?}{=}16$

$15\neq16$ ✗

Notes

No, the ordered pair is not a solution.

14. $7y-5(x+3)=12$

$7\left(\dfrac{22}{7}\right)-5(-1+3)\overset{?}{=}12$

$22-5(2)\overset{?}{=}12$

$22-10\overset{?}{=}12$

$12=12$ ✓

Yes, the ordered pair is a solution.

15. $\dfrac{y-x}{2}-3.5=1$

$\dfrac{11-2}{2}-3.5\overset{?}{=}1$

$\dfrac{9}{2}-3.5\overset{?}{=}1$

$\dfrac{9}{2}\overset{?}{=}4.5$

$9=9$ ✓

Yes, the ordered pair is a solution.

PLOTTING POINTS ON A CARTESIAN GRAPH

Plot each of the following pairs of points.

Notes

1. $(1, 3)$

2. $(4, 2)$

3. $(-2, 5)$

4. $(3, -2)$

5. $(-2, -3)$

6. $(0, 0)$

7. $(0, -5)$

8. $\left(3\frac{1}{2}, -4\frac{1}{2}\right)$

9. $(-1.5, -3.5)$

10. $\left(-1.5, 5\frac{1}{2}\right)$

Notes

Solutions

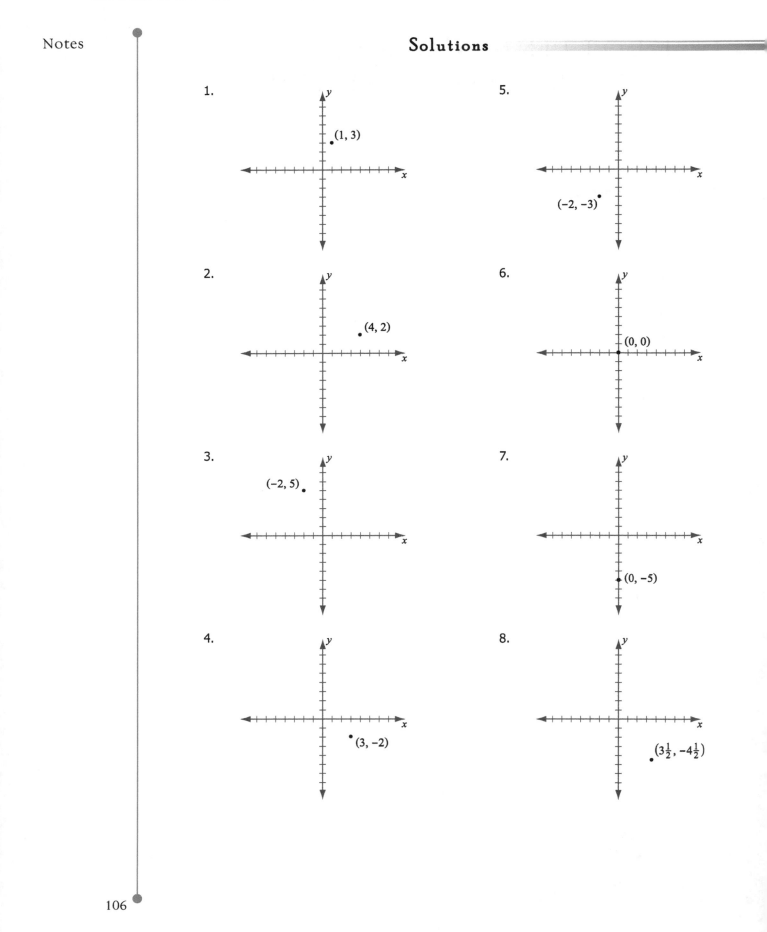

1. (1, 3)

2. (4, 2)

3. (−2, 5)

4. (3, −2)

5. (−2, −3)

6. (0, 0)

7. (0, −5)

8. $\left(3\frac{1}{2}, -4\frac{1}{2}\right)$

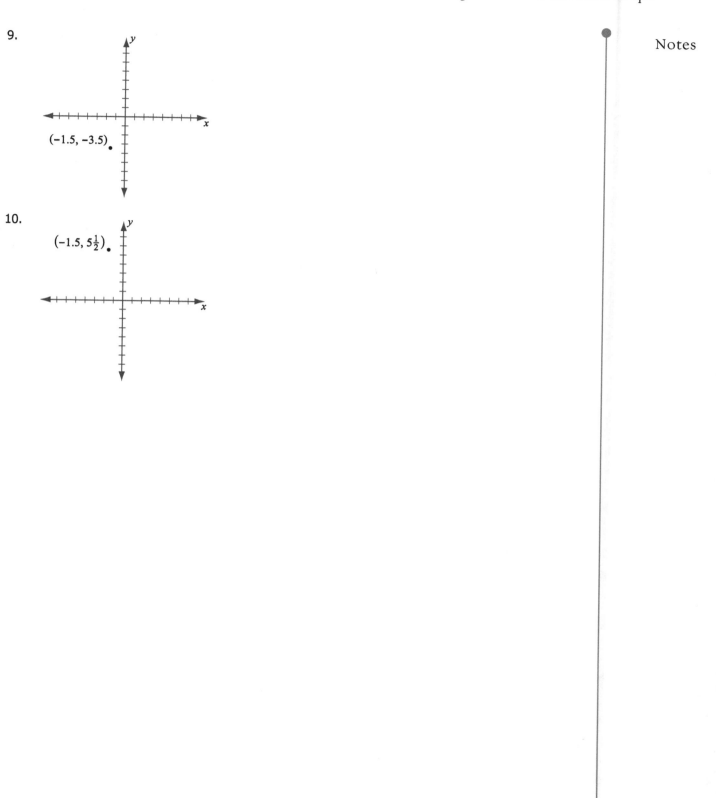

9.

(−1.5, −3.5)

10.

$(−1.5, 5\frac{1}{2})$

GRAPHING
LINEAR EQUATIONS

Plot each of the following linear equations by plotting points on the line.

1. $y = x$

2. $y = x + 2$

3. $y = -x$

4. $y = 3x$

5. $y = 4x - 1$

6. $y = -x + 5$

7. $y = \dfrac{1}{2}x$

8. $y = \dfrac{1}{2}x + 3$

9. $y = -\dfrac{1}{5}x + 2$

10. $y = 2$

11. $y = -3$

12. $y = -\dfrac{2}{3}x - \dfrac{1}{2}$

13. $y = 2.5x + 3.5$

14. $y = 0$

15. $y = \dfrac{x}{2}$

Notes

1. $y = x$

x	y
-2	-2
-1	-1
0	0
1	1
2	2

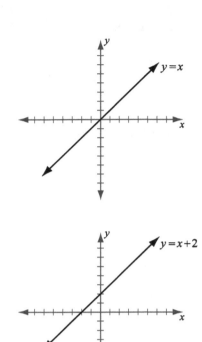

2. $y = x + 2$

x	y
-1	1
0	2
1	3
2	4

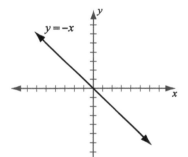

3. $y = -x$

x	y
-1	1
0	0
1	-1
2	-2

4. $y = 3x$

x	y
-1	-3
0	0
1	3
2	6

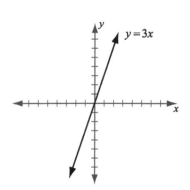

5. $y = 4x - 1$

x	y
-1	-5
0	-1
1	3
2	7

6. $y = -x + 5$

x	y
-1	6
0	5
1	4
2	3

7. $y = \frac{1}{2}x$

x	y
-2	-1
0	0
2	1

8. $y = \frac{1}{2}x + 3$

x	y
-2	2
0	3
2	4

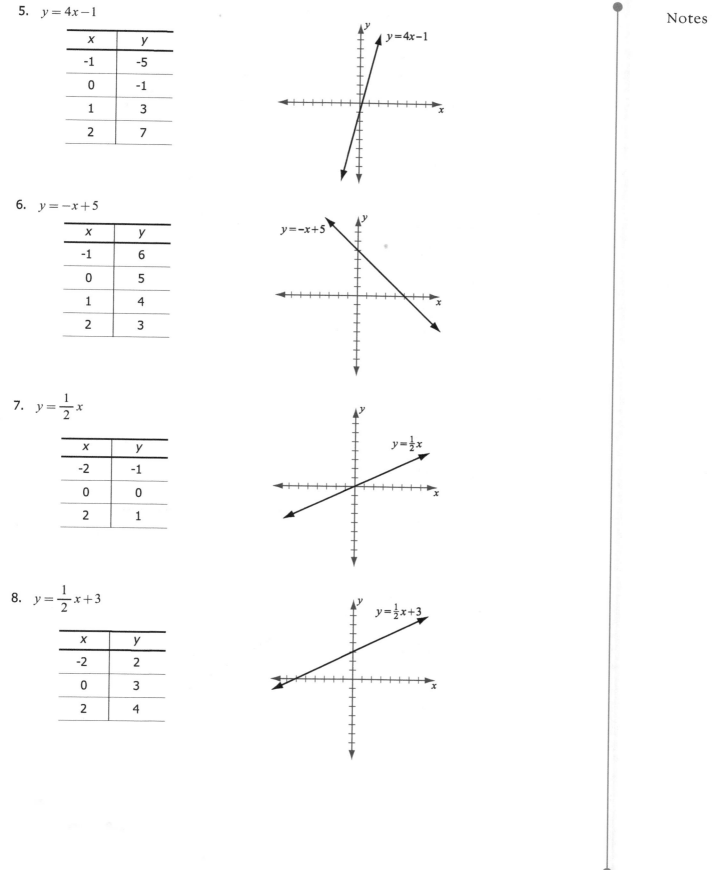

Notes

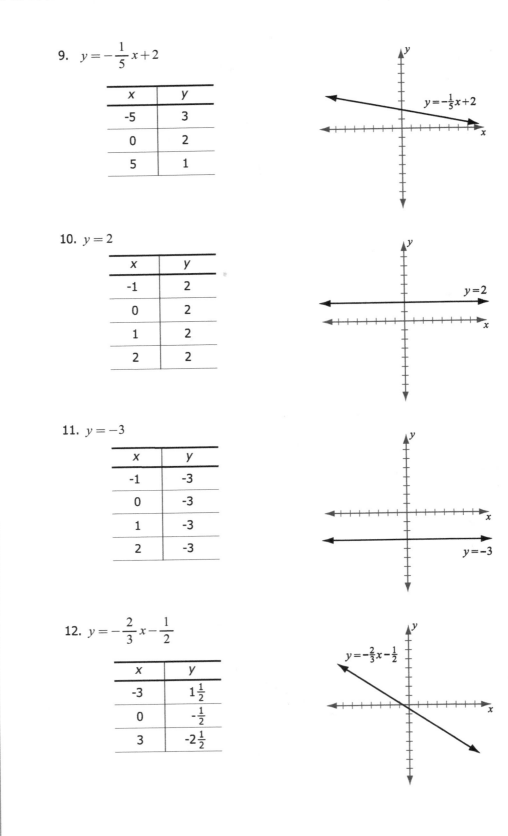

9. $y = -\frac{1}{5}x + 2$

x	y
-5	3
0	2
5	1

10. $y = 2$

x	y
-1	2
0	2
1	2
2	2

11. $y = -3$

x	y
-1	-3
0	-3
1	-3
2	-3

12. $y = -\frac{2}{3}x - \frac{1}{2}$

x	y
-3	$1\frac{1}{2}$
0	$-\frac{1}{2}$
3	$-2\frac{1}{2}$

13. $y = 2.5x + 3.5$

x	y
-1	1
0	3.5
1	6

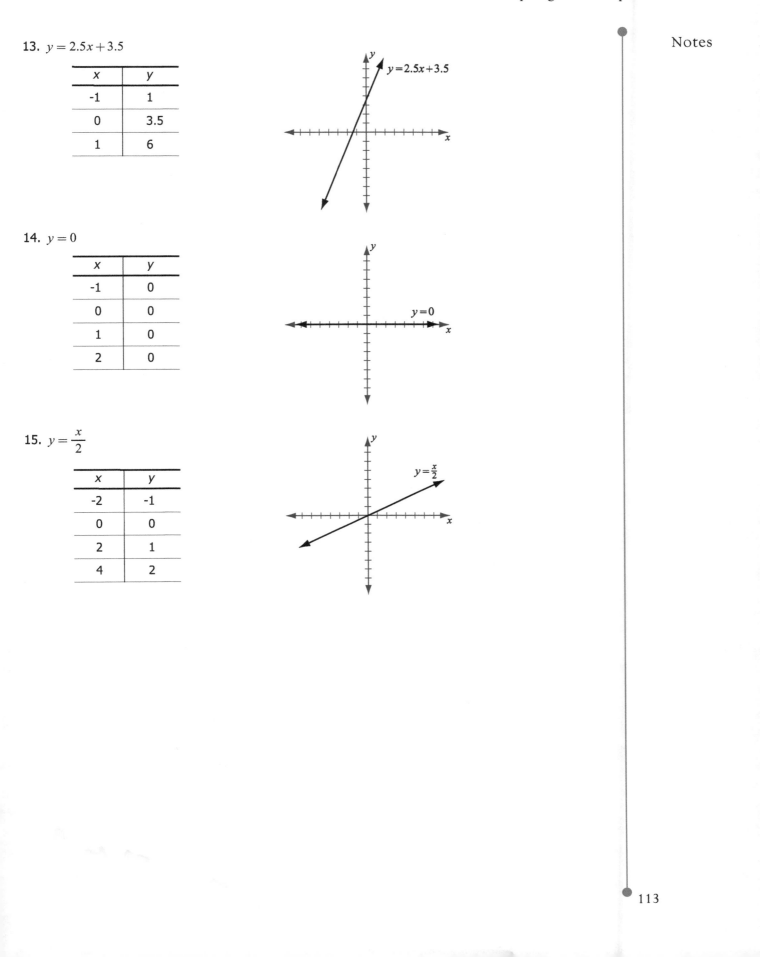

14. $y = 0$

x	y
-1	0
0	0
1	0
2	0

15. $y = \dfrac{x}{2}$

x	y
-2	-1
0	0
2	1
4	2

INTRODUCTION TO PROBABILITY

On a single roll of a die, find the probability of:

1. Rolling a 5
2. Rolling a 4
3. Rolling an even number
4. Rolling a number less than 5

From a standard deck of 52 playing cards, find the probability of drawing:

5. A 3
6. A heart
7. A card lower than a 6 (assume aces are high)
8. A face card (jack, queen, or king)

Calculate the probability of each of the following:

9. In two consecutive rolls of a die, rolling a 2 both times.

10. In two consecutive rolls of a die, rolling a 2 on the first roll and a 3 on the second roll.

11. In three consecutive rolls of a die, rolling a 5 all three times.

12. In two consecutive draws from a deck of 52 cards, drawing a heart on the first draw and a spade on the second draw. Assume that the heart is not put back into the deck after the first draw.

13. Redo Problem 12 assuming that the heart is placed back in the deck after the first draw.

14. A bag contains 3 red balls, 2 black balls, and 3 green balls. In two consecutive draws from the bag, what is the probability of drawing two black balls if:

   (a) the first black ball is not placed back in the bag after it is drawn.
   (b) the first black ball is placed back in the bag after it is drawn.

15. The United States Senate has 100 senators - two from each state. If a single vote is cast, what is the probability that the vote was cast by a senator from Pennsylvania?

Solutions

1. $\dfrac{1}{6}$

2. $\dfrac{1}{6}$

3. $\dfrac{3}{6} = \dfrac{1}{2}$

4. $\dfrac{4}{6} = \dfrac{2}{3}$

5. $\dfrac{4}{52} = \dfrac{1}{13}$

6. $\dfrac{13}{52} = \dfrac{1}{4}$

7. $\dfrac{16}{52} = \dfrac{4}{13}$

8. $\dfrac{12}{52} = \dfrac{3}{13}$

9. Since the two rolls are independent, we simply multiply the probability of each roll:
$$\frac{1}{6} \cdot \frac{1}{6} = \frac{1}{36}$$

10. Since the two rolls are independent, we simply multiply the probability of each roll:
$$\frac{1}{6} \cdot \frac{1}{6} = \frac{1}{36}$$

11. Since the three rolls are independent, we simply multiply the probability of each roll:
$$\frac{1}{6} \cdot \frac{1}{6} \cdot \frac{1}{6} = \frac{1}{216}$$

12. Since the first draw will be from a deck of 52 cards and the second draw would be from a deck of 51 cards:
$$\frac{13}{52} \cdot \frac{13}{51} = \frac{169}{2652}$$

13. Since both draws will be from a deck of 52 cards:
$$\frac{13}{52} \cdot \frac{13}{52} = \frac{169}{2704}$$

14.

(a) Since the first draw will be from a bag containing 8 balls and the second draw will be from a bag containing 7 balls:

$$\frac{2}{8} \cdot \frac{1}{7} = \frac{2}{56} = \frac{1}{28}$$

(b) Since both draws will be from a bag containing 8 balls:

$$\frac{2}{8} \cdot \frac{2}{8} = \frac{4}{64} = \frac{1}{16}$$

15. $\dfrac{2}{100} = \dfrac{1}{50}$

MEAN, MEDIAN, AND MODE

33

Find the mean for each of the following.

1. $1, 2, 3, 4, 5$

2. $-3, -2, -1, 0, 1, 2$

3. $2.5, 3.2, 6.5, 1.8$

4. $12, 64, 33, 22, 19$

5. $7, 6.28, 33.5, -20.6$

Find the median for each of the following.

6. $1, 2, 3, 4, 5$

7. $2, 4, 6, 8, 10, 12$

8. $12, 7, 13, 2, -1$

9. $6, -2, 9, -1, 10, 15$

10. $3.52, 6.37, 1.13, 2.95, 12.47$

Find the mode(s) for each of the following.

11. $0, 1, 1, 2, 3, 4$

12. $1, 2, -1, 3, 5, 2, 7, 4$

13. $-3, -1, 1, 2, 1, -3, 5, 7, 11$

14. $\dfrac{1}{2}, \dfrac{1}{4}, \dfrac{1}{3}, \dfrac{1}{4}, -\dfrac{1}{6}, \dfrac{1}{8}$

15. $2, 3, 2, 3, 2$

Answer Key

1. 3

2. $-\dfrac{1}{2}$

3. 3.5

4. 30

5. 6.545

6. 3

7. 7

8. 7

9. 7.5

10. 3.52

11. 1

12. 2

13. -3 and 1

14. $\dfrac{1}{4}$

15. 2

Solutions

1. The mean is found by adding the numbers and dividing by 5:

$$\frac{1+2+3+4+5}{5} = \frac{15}{5} = 3$$

2. The mean is found by adding the numbers and dividing by 6:

$$\frac{-3+(-2)+(-1)+0+1+2}{6} = \frac{-3}{6} = -\frac{1}{2}$$

3. The mean is found by adding the numbers and dividing by 4:

$$\frac{2.5+3.2+6.5+1.8}{4} = \frac{14}{4} = 3.5$$

4. The mean is found by adding the numbers and dividing by 5:

$$\frac{12+64+33+22+19}{5} = \frac{150}{5} = 30$$

5. The mean is found by adding the numbers and dividing by 4:

$$\frac{7+6.28+33.5+(-20.6)}{4} = \frac{26.18}{4} = 6.545$$

6. Since the numbers are already in ascending order, and the list has an odd number of entries, the median is the middle number, 3:

$$1, 2, 3, 4, 5$$
$$\uparrow$$
$$\text{median}$$

7. Since the list (which is already in ascending order) has an even number of entries, the median is found by calculating the mean of the two middle entries, 6 and 8:

$$2, 4, \underbrace{6, 8}, 10, 12$$
$$\text{two middle numbers}$$

$$\text{median}: \quad \frac{6+8}{2} = \frac{14}{2} = 7$$

8. We begin by writing the list in ascending order:

$$-1, 2, 7, 12, 13$$

Since the list has an odd number of entries, the median is the middle number, 7.

9. First, we write the list in ascending order:

$$-2, -1, 6, 9, 10, 15$$

Since the list has an even number of entries, we find the median by calculating the mean of the two middle numbers 6 and 9:

$$\text{median}: \quad \frac{6+9}{2} = \frac{15}{2} = 7.5$$

10. First, we write the list in ascending order:

$$1.13, 2.95, 3.52, 6.37, 12.47$$

Since the list has an odd number of entries, the median is the middle number, 3.52.

11. Since the number 1 appears more times than any other number in the list, 1 is the mode.

12. Since the number 2 appears more times than any other number in the list, 2 is the mode.

13. Since -3 and 1 both appear twice in the list and each of the other numbers only appears once, -3 and 1 are the modes.

14. Since the number $\frac{1}{4}$ appears more times than any other number in the list, $\frac{1}{4}$ is the mode.

15. Since the number 2 appears more times than any other number in the list, 2 is the mode.

Final Examination I

Note: In this first comprehensive final exam, the topics are grouped, but the groups are not in the same order as presented in the book.

1. $\begin{array}{r} 347 \\ + 685 \\ \hline \end{array}$

2. $1067 - 258 =$

3. $5 \times (13 \times 19) =$

4. $6 \overline{)762}$

5. Plot the following numbers on a number line:

    (a) 5

    (b) -4

    (c) 0

    (d) $2\dfrac{1}{2}$

    (e) -3.5

6. On a number line, graph the interval $(2, 7]$.

7. Find the least common multiple of each of the following:

    (a) 2, 3, 5

    (b) 4, 8, 16

8. Find the prime factorization of 120.

9. Reduce the fraction $\dfrac{42}{1470}$ to lowest terms.

10. $\dfrac{2}{3} + \dfrac{5}{9} =$

11. $\dfrac{6}{7} \times \dfrac{5}{13} =$

12. $\dfrac{\frac{7}{8}}{\frac{3}{4}} =$

13. $2\dfrac{1}{3} + 7\dfrac{1}{5} =$

14. $4\dfrac{1}{7} \times 3\dfrac{2}{5} =$

15. $\dfrac{5\frac{2}{3}}{2\frac{1}{9}} =$

16. $3.08 + 15.293 =$

17. $\begin{array}{r} 12.87 \\ -\ 7.49 \\ \hline \end{array}$

18. $\begin{array}{r} 6.24 \\ \times\ 3.985 \\ \hline \end{array}$

19. $0.6\overline{)0.102}$

20. Round 5.257 to the second decimal place.

21. Express 0.753 as a fraction.

22. Express $\dfrac{10}{80}$ as a decimal.

23. Insert the correct number into the box to make a correct proportion.

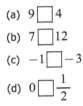

$$\frac{1}{3} = \frac{8}{\Box}$$

24. Insert the appropriate inequality symbol (>, <) into each of the following.

    (a) $9\,\Box\,4$

    (b) $7\,\Box\,12$

    (c) $-1\,\Box\,-3$

    (d) $0\,\Box\,\dfrac{1}{2}$

25. Calculate 24% of 80.

26. Calculate the exponential expression $(-2)^5$.

27. Express $\dfrac{3^{-5}}{3^{-2}}$ using a single, positive exponent.

28. Express $\sqrt{7}$ using a fractional exponent.

29. Express $9^{-5} \cdot 9^2 \cdot 9^{12}$ using a single base and positive exponent.

30. $\sqrt[3]{216} =$

31. Express $9,420,000,000$ using scientific notation.

32. Simplifying the expression

$$3^2 - 5(1-6) + (-1)(-4)$$

using the correct order of operations.

33. Insert the correct symbol $\left(\in, \notin, \subset, \not\subset\right)$ into the expression.

$$\{2, 5\}\,\square\,\{0, 1, 2, 3, 4, 5, 6\}$$

34. $\{a, b, c, d\}\cup\{x, y, z\}=$

35. Find the mean of the list $1, 3, 9, 12, 27$.

36. Find the median of the list $12, 7, 9, 3, 14, 6$.

37. Find the mode(s) of the list $2, 3, 5, 3, 5, 7, 9, 12$.

38. From a standard deck of 52 playing cards, what is the probability of drawing a 5 or a 6?

39. $\left|-5-9\right|=$

40. Simplify the algebraic expression $3\dfrac{1}{2}b+4\dfrac{1}{3}b+8b$.

41. $\left(6x^3-9x+5\right)+\left(15x^2+4x+7\right)=$

42. Solve $8x-2=14$.

43. Is the ordered pair $\left(2, 3\right)$ a solution to the equation $y=9x-15$?

44. Plot each of the following points on a Cartesian graph.

    (a) $\left(3, 6\right)$

    (b) $\left(0, -3\right)$

    (c) $\left(-4, 5\dfrac{1}{2}\right)$

45. Graph the linear equation $y=3x-2$ by plotting points.

1. 1032

2. 809

3. 1235

4. 127

5.

(a)

(b)

(c)

(d)

(e)

6.

7.

(a) 30

(b) 16

8. $120 = 2 \cdot 2 \cdot 2 \cdot 3 \cdot 5$

9. $\dfrac{1}{35}$

10. $1\dfrac{2}{9}$

11. $\dfrac{30}{91}$

12. $1\dfrac{1}{6}$

13. $9\dfrac{8}{15}$

14. $14\dfrac{3}{35}$

15. $2\dfrac{13}{19}$

16. 18.373

17. 5.38

18. 24.8664

19. 0.017

20. 5.26

21. $\dfrac{753}{1000}$

22. 0.125

23. $\dfrac{1}{3} = \dfrac{8}{\boxed{24}}$

24.
    (a) $9 \boxed{>} 4$

    (b) $7 \boxed{<} 12$

    (c) $-1 \boxed{>} -3$

    (d) $0 \boxed{<} \dfrac{1}{2}$

25. 19.2

26. -32

27. $\dfrac{1}{3^3}$

28. $7^{\frac{1}{2}}$

29. 9^9

30. 6

31. 9.42×10^9

32. 38

33. $\{2, 5\} \boxed{\subset} \{0, 1, 2, 3, 4, 5, 6\}$

34. $\{a, b, c, d, x, y, z\}$

35. 10.4

36. 8

37. 3 and 5

38. $\dfrac{2}{13}$

39. 14

40. $15\dfrac{5}{6}b$

41. $6x^3 + 15x^2 - 5x + 12$

42. $x = 2$

43. yes

44.

(a)

(b)

(c)

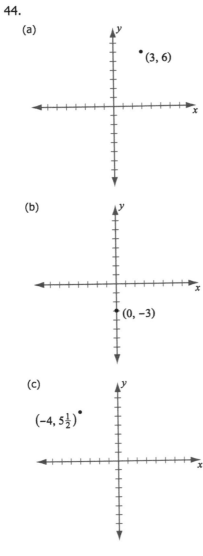

45. $y = 3x - 2$

x	y
-1	-5
0	-2
1	1
2	4

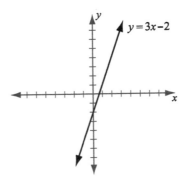

$y = 3x - 2$

1.
$$
\begin{array}{r}
347 \\
+\ 685 \\
\hline
1032
\end{array}
$$

2. $1067 - 258 = 809$

3. $5 \times (13 \times 19) = 5 \times 247 = 1235$

4.
$$
\begin{array}{r}
127 \\
6\overline{)762} \\
\underline{6}\ \ \ \\
16 \\
\underline{12} \\
42 \\
\underline{42} \\
0
\end{array}
$$

5.
(a)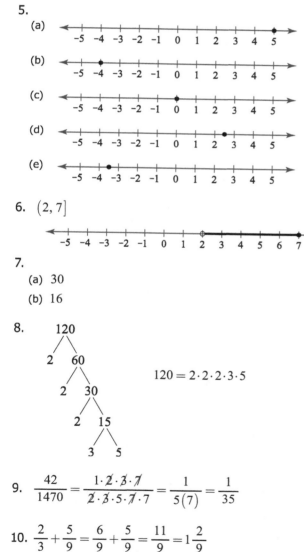

(b)

(c)

(d)

(e)

6. $(2, 7]$

7.
(a) 30

(b) 16

8.

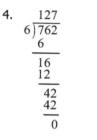

$120 = 2 \cdot 2 \cdot 2 \cdot 3 \cdot 5$

9. $\dfrac{42}{1470} = \dfrac{1 \cdot \cancel{2} \cdot \cancel{3} \cdot \cancel{7}}{\cancel{2} \cdot \cancel{3} \cdot 5 \cdot \cancel{7} \cdot 7} = \dfrac{1}{5(7)} = \dfrac{1}{35}$

10. $\dfrac{2}{3} + \dfrac{5}{9} = \dfrac{6}{9} + \dfrac{5}{9} = \dfrac{11}{9} = 1\dfrac{2}{9}$

11. $\dfrac{6}{7} \times \dfrac{5}{13} = \dfrac{6 \times 5}{7 \times 13} = \dfrac{30}{91}$

12. $\dfrac{\frac{7}{8}}{\frac{3}{4}} = \dfrac{7}{8} \times \dfrac{4}{3} = \dfrac{7 \times 4}{8 \times 3} = \dfrac{28}{24} = 1\dfrac{4}{24} = 1\dfrac{1}{6}$

13. $2\dfrac{1}{3} + 7\dfrac{1}{5} = \dfrac{7}{3} + \dfrac{36}{5} = \dfrac{35}{15} + \dfrac{108}{15} = \dfrac{143}{15} = 9\dfrac{8}{15}$

14. $4\dfrac{1}{7} \times 3\dfrac{2}{5} = \dfrac{29}{7} \times \dfrac{17}{5} = \dfrac{493}{35} = 14\dfrac{3}{35}$

15. $\dfrac{5\frac{2}{3}}{2\frac{1}{9}} = \dfrac{\frac{17}{3}}{\frac{19}{9}} = \dfrac{17}{3} \times \dfrac{9}{19} = \dfrac{17 \times 9}{3 \times 19} = \dfrac{153}{57} = 2\dfrac{39}{57} = 2\dfrac{13}{19}$

16. $3.08 + 15.293 = 18.373$

17.
$$\begin{array}{r} 12.87 \\ -\ 7.49 \\ \hline 5.38 \end{array}$$

18.
$$\begin{array}{r} 6.24 \\ \times\ 3.985 \\ \hline 24.8664 \end{array}$$

19.
$$0.6\overline{)0.102} \quad \text{quotient } 0.017$$

20. 5.26

21. $0.753 = \dfrac{753}{1000}$

22. $\dfrac{10}{80} = 10 \div 80 = 0.125$

23. $\dfrac{1}{3} = \dfrac{8}{\boxed{24}}$

24.
   (a) $9\ \boxed{>}\ 4$

   (b) $7\ \boxed{<}\ 12$

   (c) $-1\ \boxed{>}\ -3$

   (d) $0\ \boxed{<}\ \dfrac{1}{2}$

25. $0.24 \times 80 = 19.2$

26. $(-2)^5 = (-2)(-2)(-2)(-2)(-2) = -32$

27. $\dfrac{3^{-5}}{3^{-2}} = \dfrac{3^2}{3^5} = \dfrac{1}{3^3}$

28. $\sqrt{7} = 7^{\frac{1}{2}}$

29. $9^{-5} \cdot 9^2 \cdot 9^{12} = 9^{-5+2+12} = 9^9$

30. $\sqrt[3]{216} = 6$

31. $9,420,000,000 = 9.42 \times 10^9$

32. $3^2 - 5(1-6) + (-1)(-4)$

$9 - 5(1-6) + (-1)(-4)$

$9 - 5(-5) + 4$

$9 + 25 + 4$

38

33. $\{2, 5\} \boxed{\subset} \{0, 1, 2, 3, 4, 5, 6\}$

34. $\{a, b, c, d\} \cup \{x, y, z\} = \{a, b, c, d, x, y, z\}$

35. $\dfrac{1+3+9+12+27}{5} = \dfrac{52}{5} = 10.4$

36. First, we write the list in ascending order:

$$3, 6, 7, 9, 12, 14$$

Since the list has an even number of entries, the median is found by finding the mean of the two middle numbers, 7 and 9:

$$\frac{7+9}{2} = \frac{16}{2} = 8$$

37. Since the numbers 3 and 5 both appear twice in the list, while all the other numbers only appear once, 3 and 5 are the modes.

38. Since there are four 5's and four 6's in the deck there are 8 possibilities from the deck of 52 cards.

$$\frac{8}{52} = \frac{2}{13}$$

39. $|-5-9| = |-14| = 14$

40. $3\dfrac{1}{2}b + 4\dfrac{1}{3}b + 8b = 3\dfrac{3}{6}b + 4\dfrac{2}{6}b + 8b = 15\dfrac{5}{6}b$

41. $\left(6x^3 - 9x + 5\right) + \left(15x^2 + 4x + 7\right) = 6x^3 - 9x + 5 + 15x^2 + 4x + 7 = 6x^3 + 15x^2 - 5x + 12$

42. $8x - 2 = 14$

$8x - 2 + 2 = 14 + 2$

$8x = 16$

$\dfrac{8x}{8} = \dfrac{16}{8}$

$x = 2$

43. $y = 9x - 15$

$3 \overset{?}{=} 9(2) - 15$

$3 \overset{?}{=} 18 - 15$

$3 = 3$ ✓

Yes, the ordered pair is a solution.

44.

(a)

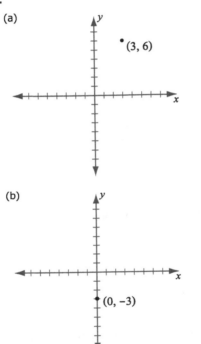

•(3, 6)

(c)

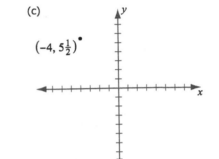

$\left(-4, 5\tfrac{1}{2}\right)$•

(b)

•(0, −3)

45. $y = 3x - 2$

x	y
-1	-5
0	-2
1	1
2	4

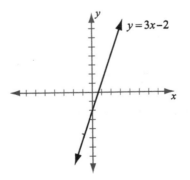

$y = 3x - 2$

Final
Examination II

Note: In this second comprehensive final exam, the topics are completely randomized so that you can see if you have grasped all of the material in the book.

1. Find the least common multiple for each of the following:

   (a) $6, 13, 17$

   (b) $7, 12, 4, 21$

2. $\begin{array}{r} 2951 \\ -\ 859 \\ \hline \end{array}$

3. Simplify the expression $(-4-3)^2 + (-1)^5 (2)$ using the correct order of operations.

4. $\left| (-2)^4 \right| =$

5. Solve $\dfrac{x-3}{5} = 2.$

6. $\dfrac{1}{3} + \dfrac{1}{4} + \dfrac{1}{5} =$

7. Round 16.5743 to the second decimal place.

8. Calculate 36% of 212.

9. $\sqrt{169} =$

10. Find the mean of the list $-4, -3, 5, 12, 68, 20.5$

11. $12\dfrac{1}{9} \times 10\dfrac{1}{15} =$

12. Express $\dfrac{2^{-5} \cdot 3^{-2}}{2^{-16} \cdot 3^{-7}}$ using only positive exponents.

13. $9.4 \times 6.53 =$

14. Graph the linear equation $y = -\dfrac{1}{3}x + 6$ by plotting points.

15. Plot the following points on a number line.

   (a) 0

   (b) -5

   (c) $6\dfrac{1}{2}$

16. $6952 + 748 =$

17. Insert the correct symbol $\left(\in, \notin, \subset, \not\subset \right)$ into the expression.

   $\{6\} \boxed{} \{\text{the set of negative real numbers}\}$

18. Is the ordered pair $(-3, 5)$ a solution to the equation $y = 7x + 12$?

19. $\dfrac{6\dfrac{1}{4}}{5\dfrac{1}{7}} =$

20. On a number line, graph the interval $[-6, -1)$.

21. Calculate the exponential expression $\left(\dfrac{1}{3}\right)^4$.

22. Plot each of the following points on a Cartesian graph.

    (a) $(1.5, -2.5)$

    (b) $\left(-3\dfrac{1}{2}, 4.5\right)$

    (c) $(-7, 0)$

23. Express 4.92 as a fraction.

24. $384 \div 12 =$

25. Express $\sqrt[4]{19}$ using a fractional exponent.

26. Find the mode(s) of the list.

$$1.5, 2.7, 3.8, -4.6, 2.7, 1.6, 3.9$$

27. $\{1, 2, 3, 4, 5, 6\} \cap \{-4, -3, -2, -1, 0, 1, 2\} =$

28. $(-12) \times (-6) \times (-7) =$

29. On a single roll of a die, what is the probability of rolling a number less than 6?

30. Find the prime factorization of 360.

31. $2.3\overline{)161}$

32. $\dfrac{5}{12} \times \dfrac{1}{17} \times \dfrac{2}{3} =$

33. Reduce the fraction $\dfrac{196}{294}$ to lowest terms.

34. $\dfrac{\dfrac{1}{13}}{\dfrac{2}{17}} =$

35. Find the median of the list $\dfrac{1}{5}, \dfrac{1}{2}, \dfrac{1}{3}, \dfrac{1}{4}$.

36. $9\dfrac{1}{6} + 8\dfrac{1}{5} =$

37. $0.997 - 2.5 =$

38. Insert the appropriate inequality symbol (>, <) into each of the following.

    (a) $\dfrac{1}{2}\ \square\ \dfrac{1}{3}$

    (b) $-2\ \square\ -3$

    (c) $0.001\ \square\ 0.01$

39. $\begin{array}{r} 17.49 \\ +\ 8.526 \\ \hline \end{array}$

40. Express $\dfrac{3}{10,000}$ as a decimal.

41. Insert the correct number into the box to make a correct proportion.

$$\frac{\square}{125} = \frac{2}{5}$$

42. Express $\left(5^{-2}\right)^{6} \cdot 5^{-4}$ using a single base and positive exponent.

43. Express 0.000000000472 using scientific notation.

44. Simplify the algebraic expression.

$$5.2x + 7.3y - 2.7y - 4.9x + 3.8z$$

45. $\left(7x^{4} - 3x^{2} + 8x\right) - \left(2x^{4} - x^{3} - 11x^{2} + 7\right) =$

1.
 (a) 1326

 (b) 84

2. 2092

3. 47

4. 16

5. $x = 13$

6. $\dfrac{47}{60}$

7. 16.57

8. 76.32

9. ± 13

10. 16.42

11. $121\dfrac{124}{135}$

12. $2^{11} \cdot 3^5$

13. 61.382

14. $y = -\dfrac{1}{3}x + 6$

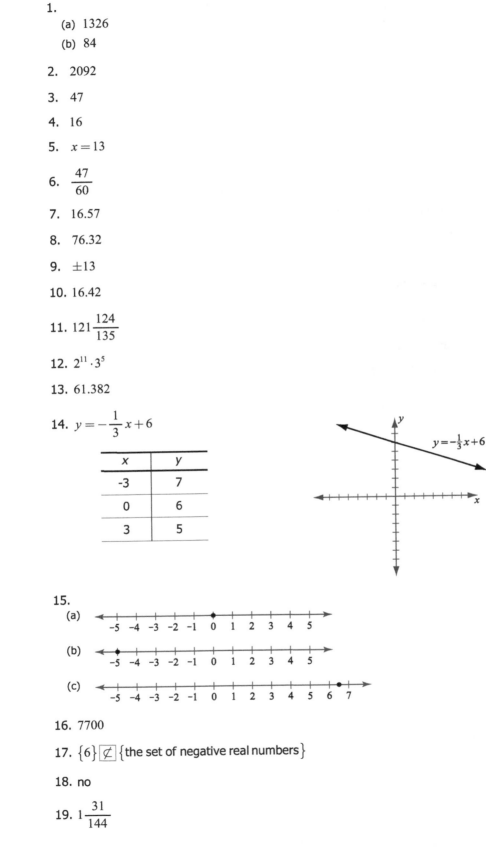

x	y
-3	7
0	6
3	5

$y = -\frac{1}{3}x + 6$

15.
 (a)

 (b)

 (c)

16. 7700

17. $\{6\}\ \not\subset\ \{\text{the set of negative real numbers}\}$

18. no

19. $1\dfrac{31}{144}$

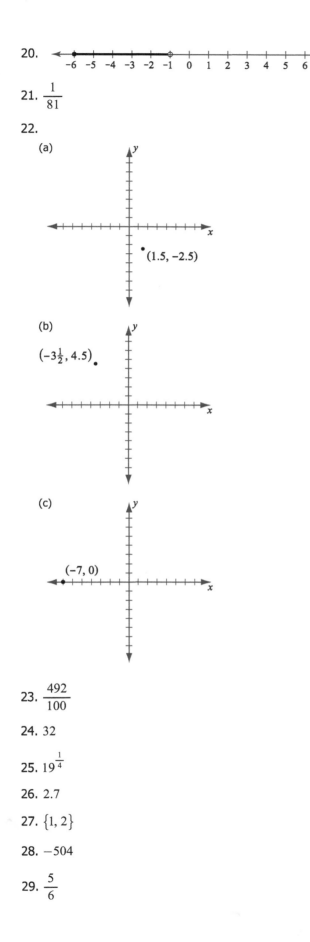

20.

21. $\dfrac{1}{81}$

22.

(a)

(b)

(c)

23. $\dfrac{492}{100}$

24. 32

25. $19^{\frac{1}{4}}$

26. 2.7

27. $\{1, 2\}$

28. -504

29. $\dfrac{5}{6}$

30. $360 = 2 \cdot 2 \cdot 2 \cdot 3 \cdot 3 \cdot 5$

31. 70

32. $\dfrac{5}{306}$

33. $\dfrac{2}{3}$

34. $\dfrac{17}{26}$

35. $\dfrac{7}{24}$

36. $17\dfrac{11}{30}$

37. -1.503

38.

(a) $\dfrac{1}{2}\boxed{>}\dfrac{1}{3}$

(b) $-2\boxed{>}-3$

(c) $0.001\boxed{<}0.01$

39. 26.016

40. 0.0003

41. $\dfrac{\boxed{50}}{125} = \dfrac{2}{5}$

42. $\dfrac{1}{5^{16}}$

43. 4.72×10^{-10}

44. $0.3x + 4.6y + 3.8z$

45. $5x^4 + x^3 + 8x^2 + 8x - 7$

1.
   (a) 1326
   (b) 84

2. $\begin{array}{r} 2951 \\ -\ 859 \\ \hline 2092 \end{array}$

3. $(-4-3)^2 + (-1)^5(2)$

   $(-7)^2 + (-1)^5(2)$

   $49 + (-1)(2)$

   $49 - 2$

   47

4. $\left|(-2)^4\right| = \left|(-2)(-2)(-2)(-2)\right| = |16| = 16$

5. $\dfrac{x-3}{5} = 2$

   $\dfrac{x-3}{5}(5) = 2(5)$

   $x - 3 = 10$

   $x - 3 + 3 = 10 + 3$

   $x = 13$

6. $\dfrac{1}{3} + \dfrac{1}{4} + \dfrac{1}{5} = \dfrac{20}{60} + \dfrac{15}{60} + \dfrac{12}{60} = \dfrac{47}{60}$

7. 16.57

8. $0.36 \times 212 = 76.32$

9. $\sqrt{169} = \pm 13$

10. $\dfrac{-4 + (-3) + 5 + 12 + 68 + 20.5}{6} = \dfrac{98.5}{6} = 16.42$

11. $12\dfrac{1}{9} \times 10\dfrac{1}{15} = \dfrac{109}{9} \times \dfrac{151}{15} = \dfrac{16459}{135} = 121\dfrac{124}{135}$

12. $\dfrac{2^{-5} \cdot 3^{-2}}{2^{-16} \cdot 3^{-7}} = \dfrac{2^{16} \cdot 3^7}{2^5 \cdot 3^2} = 2^{11} \cdot 3^5$

13. $9.4 \times 6.53 = 61.382$

14. $y = -\dfrac{1}{3}x + 6$

x	y
-3	7
0	6
3	5

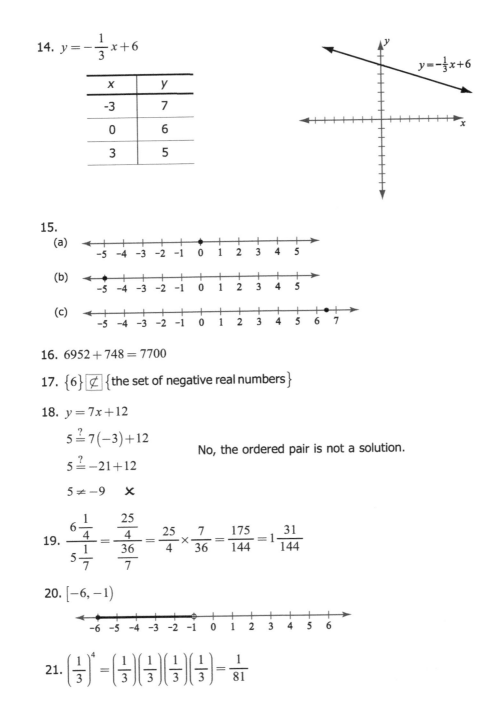

15.

(a)

(b)

(c)

16. $6952 + 748 = 7700$

17. $\{6\} \not\subset \{\text{the set of negative real numbers}\}$

18. $y = 7x + 12$

$5 \overset{?}{=} 7(-3) + 12$

$5 \overset{?}{=} -21 + 12$

$5 \neq -9 \quad \times$

No, the ordered pair is not a solution.

19. $\dfrac{6\frac{1}{4}}{5\frac{1}{7}} = \dfrac{\frac{25}{4}}{\frac{36}{7}} = \dfrac{25}{4} \times \dfrac{7}{36} = \dfrac{175}{144} = 1\dfrac{31}{144}$

20. $[-6, -1)$

21. $\left(\dfrac{1}{3}\right)^4 = \left(\dfrac{1}{3}\right)\left(\dfrac{1}{3}\right)\left(\dfrac{1}{3}\right)\left(\dfrac{1}{3}\right) = \dfrac{1}{81}$

22.

(a)

(b)

(c)

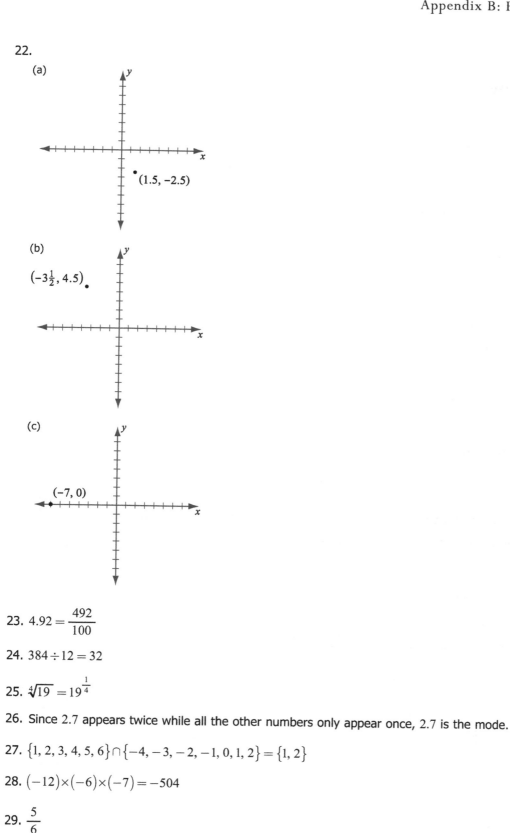

23. $4.92 = \dfrac{492}{100}$

24. $384 \div 12 = 32$

25. $\sqrt[4]{19} = 19^{\frac{1}{4}}$

26. Since 2.7 appears twice while all the other numbers only appear once, 2.7 is the mode.

27. $\{1, 2, 3, 4, 5, 6\} \cap \{-4, -3, -2, -1, 0, 1, 2\} = \{1, 2\}$

28. $(-12) \times (-6) \times (-7) = -504$

29. $\dfrac{5}{6}$

30.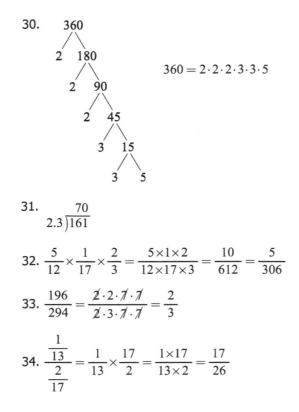

$$360 = 2 \cdot 2 \cdot 2 \cdot 3 \cdot 3 \cdot 5$$

31. $2.3\overline{)161}$ with quotient 70

32. $\dfrac{5}{12} \times \dfrac{1}{17} \times \dfrac{2}{3} = \dfrac{5 \times 1 \times 2}{12 \times 17 \times 3} = \dfrac{10}{612} = \dfrac{5}{306}$

33. $\dfrac{196}{294} = \dfrac{\cancel{2} \cdot 2 \cdot \cancel{7} \cdot \cancel{7}}{\cancel{2} \cdot 3 \cdot \cancel{7} \cdot \cancel{7}} = \dfrac{2}{3}$

34. $\dfrac{\frac{1}{13}}{\frac{2}{17}} = \dfrac{1}{13} \times \dfrac{17}{2} = \dfrac{1 \times 17}{13 \times 2} = \dfrac{17}{26}$

35. First, we write the list in ascending order:

$$\frac{1}{5}, \frac{1}{4}, \frac{1}{3}, \frac{1}{2}$$

Since the list has an even number of entries, the median is found by finding the mean of the two middle entries, $\dfrac{1}{4}$ and $\dfrac{1}{3}$:

$$\dfrac{\frac{1}{4} + \frac{1}{3}}{2} = \dfrac{\frac{3}{12} + \frac{4}{12}}{2} = \dfrac{\frac{7}{12}}{2} = \dfrac{7}{12} \times \dfrac{1}{2} = \dfrac{7}{24}$$

36. $9\dfrac{1}{6} + 8\dfrac{1}{5} = \dfrac{55}{6} + \dfrac{41}{5} = \dfrac{275}{30} + \dfrac{246}{30} = \dfrac{521}{30} = 17\dfrac{11}{30}$

37. $0.997 - 2.5 = -1.503$

38.

(a) $\dfrac{1}{2} \boxed{>} \dfrac{1}{3}$

(b) $-2 \boxed{>} -3$

(c) $0.001 \boxed{<} 0.01$

39.
$$
\begin{array}{r}
17.49 \\
+\ 8.526 \\
\hline
26.016
\end{array}
$$

40. $\dfrac{3}{10,000} = 3 \div 10,000 = 0.0003$

41. $\dfrac{\boxed{50}}{125} = \dfrac{2}{5}$

42. $\left(5^{-2}\right)^6 \cdot 5^{-4} = 5^{-12} \cdot 5^{-4} = 5^{-16} = \dfrac{1}{5^{16}}$

43. $0.000000000472 = 4.72 \times 10^{-10}$

44. $5.2x + 7.3y - 2.7y - 4.9x + 3.8z = 0.3x + 4.6y + 3.8z$

45. $\left(7x^4 - 3x^2 + 8x\right) - \left(2x^4 - x^3 - 11x^2 + 7\right) = 7x^4 - 3x^2 + 8x - 2x^4 + x^3 + 11x^2 - 7$

$$= 5x^4 + x^3 + 8x^2 + 8x - 7$$